Native Daughter

The life and times of a Jamaican woman of the soil

Z. Nia Reynolds

First published 2000 by
MACMILLAN EDUCATION LTD
London and Oxford
Companies and representatives throughout the world

www.macmillan-caribbean.com

ISBN 0-333-74027-0

10	9	8	7	6	5	4	3	2	1
09	08	07	06	05	04	03	02	01	00

This book is printed on paper suitable for recycling and made from fully managed and sustained forest sources.

Typeset by Dave Glover

Printed in Hong Kong

A catalogue record for this book is available from the British Library.

Illustrations by Judy Stevens

Acknowledgements
The author and publishers wish to acknowledge, with thanks, the following photographic sources:
Black Stock
Royal Geographical Society

The author and publishers would like to acknowledge, with thanks, permission to use the following songs:
'Day-O', 'Come Back Liza', 'Jamaica Farewell', 'The Jackass Song' and 'Hosanna' ('I Build a House'). Composed by Irving Burgie, published world-wide by Cherry Lane Music Publishing Company Inc and administered in the UK and Eire by Global Chrysalis Music Publishing Co. Ltd
Lyrics from 'Matilda' (SPAN) by kind permission of Universal Music Publishing Ltd

Cover photo: *Among the mangoes at Martinique* by Paul Gaugin,

Do not rejoice over me, my enemy:
when I fall, I *shall* rise ...

– Micah

For Bawling

List of plates

A Jamaican artisan showing a fan he has made

Yabba pots (earthenware vessels) for sale. The word *yabba* originates from the Twi word *ayawa*

Portrait of a Haitian man taken in 1908/9

A Caribbean country scene at the turn of the nineteenth century. Note the market women with their goods, atop their heads, off to trade

Wash day by the river with clothing laid out to bleach in the sun

In the cool of the evening ... a humble country homestead

Two Jamaican boys picking oranges, taken towards the end of the nineteenth century

A community of East Indians in Jamaica threshing rice (1890s)

Workers on a sugar estate. Note the *bushas* (overseers) on horseback. Brutal conditions often led to cane-fields being torched

A Jamaican farmer or beekeeper tending his ground at the turn of the nineteenth century. He is growing cassava and dasheen. Note the bee-box for producing honey in the foreground. This type of cultivation was practised by many country people producing crops such as sugar, coffee, cocoa, rum and pimento to achieve self-sufficiency

Maroon boys gathering fire-wood in Portland

Maroon father and child at Nanny Town (Moore Town)

Market bound with jelly coconuts

Homeward bound from market with his bankra baskets, a Jamaican farmer rides through a banana walk in Eastern Jamaica

Remembering the days of the old school yard, a scene outside a Jamaican country school run by a Christian organisation

Posed images of Jamaicans taken during the nineteenth century. Many images of this type were taken by tourists or by missionary societies

'Cheers, mate!' This contrived image of Jamaican boys would have been used as a picture postcard in its day (late 1900s)

Bitter harvest ... plantation labour in Jamaica's cane-fields during slavery was often brutal and inhuman. After emancipation, many small landowners cultivated their 'cane piece', producing crops for market and for making rum and sugar

Many of these images were taken by Harry Johnston, an anthropologist who set out to document the lives of Caribbean people between 1908 and 1909. The images, recently 'discovered' at the Royal Geographical Society, form part of a valuable archive. Although for the most part this type of anthropological survey was decidedly racist and patronising, these images are a testament to the beauty and creativity of Black Caribbean people.

Contents

Introduction

> I've known rivers:
> I've known rivers ancient as the world
> and older than the flow of human blood
> in human veins.
> My soul has grown deep like the rivers
>   – Langston Hughes
>   *The Negro Speaks of Rivers*

> Ole time someting come back again
>   – Anon

It has been said that when an old person dies, it is like a library burning down. Mindful of this, and captivated by the many fascinating stories – and their equally fascinating storytellers – in the Caribbean, I set out to write about one woman, who can fittingly be counted amongst the griots or 'living libraries' of Jamaica.

Native Daughter is a personal chronicle, a narrative told in the first person, but it is also about a generation of *native* sons and daughters, portrayed in a way that is part memoir, part a history of Jamaica. It scarcely matters that the narrator is neither famous nor notorious. What matters is documenting, for posterity, the vital history which she, and others like her, encapsulate and are able to relate; the essence of Jamaican-ness.

Emily Bailey, the eponymous *Native Daughter* of the title, was born in 1900, in the parish of Westmoreland, at the western-most point of Jamaica. As the poem says, she has 'known rivers' – rivers of change, and yet also of continuity as the old, familiar ways of culture and tradition co-exist alongside encroaching urbanisation and even globalisation; as the incongruous sight of satellite dishes scattered atop village shacks testifies.

Native Daughter is the life story of Emily Bailey, and is not written solely in her Jamaican patois; a language alive with feeling, rhythm and humour; there is a fusing of the language with standard English. Just as the special structure of a raw silk or linen garment produces intrinsic wrinkles, crinkles and slubs as a natural sign of the material's authenticity, so too does the language in *Native Daughter* reflect the bona fide characteristics of the narrator, the culture and the people. Emily's native tongue is as integral a part of her being as the land and all it yields. There are certain situations in which the substitution of standard English for raw Jamaican would cause the sense, the humour and the vibrancy to be lost. So, for this reason, there is an impressionistic fusion of the two. At times the text is presented in the most standard of English, whilst at others, it is in patois; on other occasions there is hybridity. It is a very oral language and I think no authenticity of the experiences related in the story is tarnished by the written hybridisation. It is all relevant, and the issue isn't about compromising or cowardice, although there were inevitable considerations about making the work accessible to a wide audience without losing the essential, *artical* heart of it. Patois is a language which, although spoken by thousands, few have the opportunity to read. The book should prove a challenge and an inspiration to all people interested in Jamaica's culture and heritage, and in the vernacular. I was intrigued to record so many fascinating words, some of which are now obsolete. A pot-pourri of tongues, 'twangs', and dialects, African, French, Spanish, English, Portuguese and Scottish, the Jamaican language has virtually discarded its old reputation as being a bastardisation of English. Since the sixties and seventies and even earlier, the Jamaican language has attained wordwide audiences through calypso, ska and especially the reggae of Bob Marley and many others, as well as its offshoots, like rap. The pioneering work of writers and performers like Louise Bennett-Coverley in promoting the language and the value of it, can also never be understated.

Native Daughter is about a woman who has witnessed spectacular changes in this century: flight, rocket ships, the exploration of space, trains and planes and automobiles, the phone, the fax, television. A world in transition and at war. Yet her generation have somehow remained untouched by the stress of it all, and they have rarely had the opportunity to relate their experiences for the benefit of one another and for the generations to come. Amidst a rapidly developing culture speeded up by eclectic mass communications, the voices of *the elders*, the traditional griots and orators in African/Caribbean societies, have become increasingly muted. Their passing is met with some belated consternation that no record was made of their stories and experiences. The effect of this is particularly bitter if the former ways of the elders are scorned or devalued in favour of Western culture. This is where I come in, attempting to gather and record their tales and folklore.

The inspiration for this story came chiefly from my grandmother, a charismatic Jamaican woman called Emily Lawson, who, like her namesake in the book, was born at the turn of the century. A more pleasant, humble and gentle person I could not have hoped to find, with formidable inner strength and patience like refined gold. I spent many hours with Emily listening to her stories and piecing the episodes together, my imagination revelling in the vibrant backdrop of places and events she recollected. The process of creating *Native Daughter* was not unlike the painstaking yet devoted way in which Emily approached her craft of patchwork quilt-making; that in itself was something to behold; the way she undertook the task with such diligence and sober perfectionism. But, as is the way of most wise heads, this gentle lady was never one to seek an audience and so I had to 'bribe' her much of the time.

I would prepare her breakfast: 'What would you like today, coffee or some cocoa-tea?'

'Gi' mi mi coffee, man, an' mek sure it well strong,' she would reply, and I would oblige, adding some hard-dough bread, Excelsior crackers, bulla cake or another favourite Jamaican morsel for her delectation, and then waiting for what seemed like ages for her to finish eating so we could, as it were, 'chew the fat'.

Her stories and story-telling were compelling. Before long breakfast would flow into lunch time without either the stories drying up or interest lost in her patchwork chore. As evening closed in on us, not even the fading light of sunset would make her put her work down, or stop the flow of recollecting 'ole time story' till such a time as seemed appropriate to her. And then, once the last stitch had been sewn and the last sentence spoken, nothing could compel her to add or extract a stitch or a word. Like most old people, whilst she could hardly remember (or indeed have *cared* to recount) the events of one or two days previously, she had little trouble reeling off in minute detail, events that had taken place some fifty, sixty or even seventy years ago. And in later life wherever she travelled, mostly to the UK or US, she lived the adage that you can take the woman out of the country but not the country out of the woman. But that's another story for another time. For all the novelty and advantages of being 'a-foreign', sure enough a time would come when her feet would start itching and homesickness would set in.

Asked during her advancing years how she would make it up to her own rocky mountain home in the country, she would square her shoulders defiantly and reply, 'Don't you worry, for I know de road and de road know me.'

Such was the indefatigability of her spirit she might have been telling me, '*Why, the world's my oyster which I with sword will open!*'

Native Daughter was primarily conceived as a tribute to Emily Lawson, a tremendous matriarch; whose life was forged of struggle and fire. It is also dedicated to the men and women of her generation, and to the memories of all native African-Jamaican sons and daughters of our yesterday, our today and to those living libraries – griots – of our tomorrow.

Native Daughter is about love and sacrifice, hope and pride; about a people as strong and solid as 'the rock' that is Jamaica.

A so mi buy it, a so mi sell it.

Z. Nia Reynolds

Acknowledgements

Thanks to the Creator for the greatest love of all. Heartfelt thanks and good wishes to the Lawson family, Mah, Emily Adina, SSLPS, Muzzo, Tony Drummie, Peter 'Che', Taata, Victor the history man and singer-man, my family and everyone else not mentioned who sat with me and shared experiences and stories and those who just plain tolerated my obsession with foklore. And a special dedication to Chlo, Dan-the-man, Babbajo and the ones still to come: Be proud of who you are and always remember, you have already won.

Further Reading

Cassidy, Frederic G., *Jamaica Talk*, Macmillan Caribbean.
Cassidy and Le Page, *Dictionary of Jamaican English*, Cambridge.
Bennett-Coverley, Louise, *Jamaica Labrish*, Sangster's Book Stores.
Gates, Brian (ed.), *Afro-Caribbean Religions*.
Hurston, Zora Neale, *Tell My Horse*, Perennial Library, Harper and Row.
Morrish, Ivor, *Obeah, Christ and Rastaman*, James Clark.

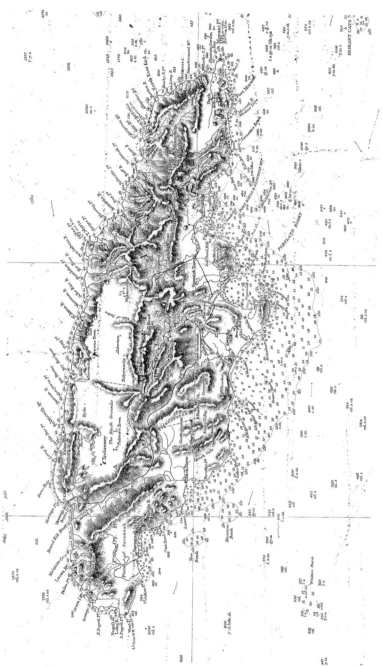

Map of Jamaica from 1912 [Royal Geographical Society]

BOOK

1

1

Many Rivers to Cross

Dead an' wake

You know, they say when me did born, me never had any hair 'pon me head. True; clean bald, no hair whatsoever, not a strand; all because of the eczema that covered me from the crown of me head right down to the soles of me feet; all over. It even reach right down inside me throat.

Ole Jane, me madda, said when they used to pick me up to bathe me and wash me mouth, all you could hear from me was, 'uuuuurrggghh!' because it was so painful.

They had to be handling me more delicately than the usual newborn suckling on account of my condition. Everybody must have been tip-toeing round the place like I was a new-laid egg they were all anxious over.

I don't know for certain what I was suffering with. Talk have it one time seh it was *mirasmi* me did have. All I know is that I was a sickly babe; sick unto dying as I would later get to understand.

Maama – Ole Jane – had to get a fine piece o' *claat* and wash out me mouth and down inside the throat with a mixture of aloes and water. As she did that, I would cry out and my throat would bleed.

Ole Jane said one time she had just finished bathing me and afterwards, she oiled me all over and put me to lie down. Little while later when she came to feed me, she said I was just stretched right out like me did dead.

She cried out, 'Lawd, Natty, see the pickney a-dead 'pon me!'

Now, Natty, my father, was a quiet, humble man, who did always take his time over everything; he never used to fuss-fuss or be quick to get excited.

So while she *dideh* a-fret and a-carry on, him just say, 'Jane, a consider me a consider wha' fi do.'

He was trying to be cool as ice, but this time he just sat down outside with his hands 'pon him head a worry like hell over the matter.

So, as the story goes, me *li'dung* stiff like me did dead; stretched right out like a corpse. And it seemed that after they did everything they could to try and revive me, the two of them gave up hope altogether.

As the evening began to draw in, painting the sky with the blazing hues of sunset, Ole Nat tek time go outside in the yard, picked up his old fork and started to dig – a bury dem decide seh dem a-go bury me now, yu know!

It wasn't the first time the old people would have been burying one of their offsprings. They had seen it before: stillbirth, sickness in infancy, even disease sometimes, wiping out the life of two or three young ones.

They themselves were healthy and strong, but *pickney* coming into the world arrive with no warranty or assurance, and nobody, young or old, can ever be certain they are going to live to see three score years and ten.

Anyway, as Natty made the first big plunge with the fork, stabbing into the soft soil to start the grave – my grave – Ole Jane said I made a sound like 'aaargggh!' and then, I just sneezed.

She bawled out: 'Natty, run come quick, Emel no dead.'

You could just imagine what manner of jubilation they did carry on with and from that, they decided to call me 'Dead an' Wake'.

There is a plant which goes by that name, although some people know it as *shame-a-Macca*, or *shame-a-Lady*. As soon as anybody goes to make contact with it, it just folds right up and soon afterwards, it just opens right back out again when the intruder's gone. *A mussi* that dem christened me after.

But Old Jane said it was no small amount of nourishment it took just to bring me up; it was plenty banana porridge, cornmeal porridge and goat's milk that helped strengthen me and bring me safely back from the brink.

One time, when me was still 'lickle bit', a womăn named Hannah Mitchell saw me coming from Redpan with a two-and-sixpence pudding pan full o' water 'pon me head and she bawled out, 'Look Dead an' Wake! Emel, a-yu dat or a-yu *duppy*?' She was so shocked to see me, for remember, is common knowledge that I was on the doorstep of death; in the valley of the shadow of death, man.

It was the 22nd of June 1900 that I came to see the sun and to take my place in the family of Maas Natty and Maama Jane. Little most sickness caused me to die before time, but by Gaad's grace that was not to be.

Not too long after that, the name 'Dead an' Wake' just fastened on amongst people in the district. All who saw me told the story, 'as fa dat lickle one, she never *baan* fi dead'.

Family tree

Nathaniel, my *faada*, who they called Maas Nat or Natty, was a ground worker, what some might want to call farmer. A hard worker too, you know, every day all throughout his life.

Natty's father's name was John Ashwood and he lived over at Colodyn. I used to go over deh from time to time as a pickney to look for my grandfather. He used to suffer with asthma, I remember that; how oftentimes he used to be short of breath. One or two times he would take a draw from off his *asthma cigar*.

His own father's name was 'Old Hay', and he was one of those old time enslaved people, born during slavery time, although the story goes how he was amongst the bold ones who did run away and set himself up in the hills with his family along with some other bravehearts.

I think his rightful name was Thomas, but I am not certain. We never got to know too much about him directly, but we knew for sure that those old-time people lived through brutality and too much hardship under the whip. Hardship man, in every sense of the word, and it followed right through to we who were born long after slavery did done.

Even as a child, it made me proud to know that Old Hay, my ancestor, really stood up to the slave-drivers, and went as far as to take his family out from plantation brutality and go set up his *palenque* way up in the hills. Still, it was a fearsome kind of pride which you wouldn't dare tell another soul in case they told you that you had no right to feel such a way.

Old Hay was every bit a *maroon*. Hearing talk of him amongst the older folks made me feel so swell-headed and put me in mind of our proud tradition of freedom fighters like Accompong Nanny who did fight 'gainst the English and did use her *batty* to catch bullets before she fired them off back to kill the enemy. Marvellous talk about such deeds urged me deep within myself to press on to find my own destiny. Even at a tender age, I knew whatever that destiny would be I would always be free.

My grandfather, John, had a place up at Bun Hill, a rough old area where they worked the land. Sun up to sun down, hard work is all poor people knew about.

As it happened, my grandfather never liked my father, Nathaniel, his own son, and when it came time to portion out the property to his children, it was a little piece o' land quite down *inna* the gully bottom they decided to give him. You can't imagine how hard it was to try and make something out of it. There were rock-stones and bushes all over and when night came down all you could hear was *bare so-so toad a croak*. The place was just so dark and miserable you couldn't tell when the sun came up and when it went back down.

All the family agreed that was where poor Natty was to go; his choice never came into it at all. Ole Nat did come in like a slave to them; anything they said he had to jump. They felt they could treat him any and any-how, and because he was such a meek and humble man who never bothered to complain, they took that as encouragement to man-handle him.

All that went on for a time, but as the saying goes, '*provocation mek dummy man talk*'. Eventually, Natty decided enough was enough, and let them know plain seh him a no pickney. He couldn't put up with the place they gave him, so he managed to find a place for himself over at Hobson Spring. This time it was a piece of land no bigger than a hand middle him go get. That was all he was able to afford at the time. All the same, little bit or not, it belonged to him. He never had to worry about living 'pon anybody *eye-top* again.

Some of Maas Nat's sisters were really stand-offish and *stoush*. They never treated Nat with any kind of respect whatsoever. Even when John, their father, died, they never even bothered to tell Natty.

In those days people could stand up on Bun Hill and announce whatever news was going on, and you could hear it right down at Ashwood yard. Eventually when Natty did get the news about his father, it was the same way he passed it on; he stood up on the hill and broadcast it. Poor Nat never wept, he saved his eye-water for inside his own yard when nobody could see him a cry.

People used to say Natty's family never liked him because of his wife, Jane. Some felt she was too proud and even went as far as to call her, 'de red bitch'. But, you know, it wasn't her my father was going to marry. It was a different lady named Campbell, Fran Campbell.

When we were growing up, Old Nat would always *siddung* – especially when him belly full – and tell us some old time stories: like how he and our mother, Jane, came to be together.

What happened was, Nat and the others used to work out, breaking rock-stones and that kind of hard labour for *backra* to use to build roads and such like. The *Parochial Board* used to provide that employment to teams or gangs of workers, contracting out the labour by the chain which was 22 yards. The women had the job of breaking the stone, while the men would use the broken stone to 'pack' the roadway. The women would also take charge of the cooking by the roadside, and the whole affair, although it was hard-labour, was run with great co-operation, and as they worked, they would sing songs:

> Dally down a manuel road
> gal an' bwoy
> fi go bruk rock-stone
> gal an' bwoy
> bruk-a dem one by one
> gal an' bwoy
> bruk-a dem two by two
> gal an' bwoy

Anyway, come the end of the week it was pay day. They would all go a-office and line up to get their money and this one time Fran Campbell arranged to collect Natty's payment. When she got it, I can't remember whether it was penny or *tuppy* or how much she took, but she did go in the money. A little while later, when time come for him to get it from her, Natty saw that some was missing. When he asked her about it she told him how she saw something she did well want and took the money to buy it. Mass Nat never liked that at all.

He told her, 'I don't have no use fi yu. If yu tief a *quatty* you wi' tief more, for from you go in de money without asking is stealing. I don't want no tief to be my wife.'

But while him a-talk that, he was looking at Jane same time, to make sure she got the same message.

Now, Jane was fat and red-skin and her people came from over Bronte. Her mother's name was Frances Scarlett, and she was big and red too, but short with pretty Indian hair. Frances was married to Eddie Scarlett, my other grandfather, who was short and clumsy and everyone used to call him 'Uncle Eddie'.

In those days, Maas Nat used to play a concertina, and whenever you heard him go out and play, young people would get up to dance. *Bwoy*, that would be something to see; a time of jubilation and excitement.

That's how he got to find out that Jane was a good dancer. Back in those times it was the *quadrille* they used to dance. Now, way down in the evening while everybody was lost in the entertainment, Maas Nat took Jane aside and told her it wasn't she he was looking at but how the other woman let him down. A so him propose.

He told Jane, 'If yu know yu not *arnest*, no *badda* look fi me to marry yu.'

She, however, was besotted, and that is how my mother and father came together. He always let her know that she was not his first choice but how he came to pick her after Fran Campbell 'turn tief'.

All in all, is fourteen children Maas Nat and Ole Jane had, but not all of us lived, through mishaps and all dem way deh. The eight of us who grew up were Florence, David, Louisa, Cornelius, Elvira, Alice, me and then my brother Walter.

The *heap o' we* lived in one little house that Maas Natty built in a small district in Westmoreland, surrounded all around by hills and gullies and covered over by a sky so blue and a sun so hot it would a come in like a portion of heaven, if only we never had to strive so much.

The irony with the land is how easy it is to misunderstand it. One minute, it would come in kind like your bosom friend and you could almost imagine that all you had to do after eating a fruit, was just spit out the seeds on the ground in the morning and by evening you would expect to see the seeds sprouting and taking root. But, another time, you felt like that same soil was your sworn enemy, how it came in dry, tough and malicious; when *dutty* tough and all who working it cried with pain and mumbled about how Ham was cursed so that was why we, his black descendants, bore a heavy burden and would only ever be 'hewers of wood and drawers of water'!

Growing up, we had a hard life. Ole time people bear testimony to what it means to earn dem bread by the sweat of dem brow. We meet poverty face to face; who feels it knows it.

I tell you, my road rough and tough, it no run straight through.

Home circle

Jane's brothers and sisters were: Samuel, Albert, Joe, Nathan, Queenie, Martha, Rosanne, Marian, Princess and Christie. On my father's side, Charles Nathaniel Ashwood, who everybody called 'Maas Nat' or 'Brother Natty', had his set of sisters, but he didn't have any brothers at all; he was the only boy. He had a half sister called Cassandra but everybody used to call her 'Ione' or 'Miss Cass'. Then there was Sarah, Flor, Lily – who was my godmother – and Bertha, who was a teacher.

Uncle Sam and Uncle Albert were my favourites, or as we would say, 'me good uncles'. As a child, I always used to get stories about what and what they used to get on with in their youth like this one experience.

Now, just below where Ma Fanny lived there was a meeting house and they always used to hold church gatherings and other functions there.

As it happened, one time a visiting preacher came to the area and the meeting hall was packed out. People used to come from all over to those crusades and on this occasion everybody in Ma Fanny's household went to the rally. Anyway, the preacher a-preach, a-preach, and people a-listen quite keenly and some all-a get moved in the spirit and others convicted to repentance. So, while the preacher man a-preach strong-strong, getting ready to mek *altar call*, the choir struck up with, 'O, weary heart, oppressed with sin; won't you let me come in?'

Uncle Albert mumbled to himself: 'Oh weary heart oppressed wid sin, won't you let me in?', mimicking the preacher. Then hear him, 'Cho! every day *fi-unno* heart oppressed wid sin, how fi-me never oppress yet?' and he took himself out of the meeting hall, *gaan* him gaan home. This time a-'member him remember seh the sugar pan hang up in the house, so is that him gaan home for.

Now, a couple of the others took time following tip-toe behind Albert till him ketch up a-house. When he reached, he went in the room and climbed up to where the sugar pan was hanging up in the ceiling, way out of sight. He quietly took it down and just as he went to dip his hand in it, they bawled out: 'A ketch yu!' Man, the jump Uncle Albert jump! Now, he used to stammer and with the shock Uncle Albert stuttered couple words then told them 'Is test me come to test the sugar fi mek sure it sweet.' As he said so, him lick him tongue like *ke-ke*, and they had no choice but to laugh. They couldn't bother to beat Uncle Albert after that for how he amused them. And, after all, they decided that he told the truth!

Now, Uncle Albert was one big coward when it come to getting a beating. It was common knowledge around the district how him did 'fraid a beating! But he was always willing to do anything his mama did want him to do, or else to follow her anywhere she was going like a loyal puppy, so most times that helped to perserve his hide.

Uncle Joe, now, was always teasing and provoking Albert to fight because he knew that Albert was short of temper. Through that, Ma Fanny used to always carry Albert with her everywhere to keep him out of trouble.

Uncle Albert had a godfather who came from over Briscoe, but Albert misheard and called it 'Brochas'. To get joke, they use to say to Uncle Albert, 'Which part yu call Brochas?'

Hear him: 'Whe' p-p-p-p-plenty p-panana pear.' They would laugh after him because, not only did the poor fellow stammer but he said, 'panana pear' when him did mean to say, 'banana bear'. Because he couldn't talk good, they took whatever he said to form joke, but Albert never took it to heart. Him wasn't tall, him did short, and Joe now, he was tall and slim, and the two of them did always a-fight or a-quarrel, mostly because of Joe's provocation.

All of her children took after Maama's red colour except Albert who was black-skinned.

I remember a song my uncles used to sing when it was crab season and the big pot of crab did deh 'pon fire. It go so: 'Come butter, come fat,' and when you knocked the back of those big crabs, you would just see a whole heap of fat coming out. As a pickney, I did always love to go round deh when crab did a-cook. To this day, there is nothing to me like fresh crab eaten with loving company.

Old time people used to take every situation and make a song or else have a song for every situation. When my uncles were waiting for the dinner to be ready, they used to sing. One would strike up: 'Mi-a knock mi knee.' And the other person would sing: 'Mi-a knock mi shin.'

That would be Uncle Joe and Uncle Sam; they couldn't wait. It was their *paki* they were knocking against their knee and shin and as they sang, they knocked, as they knocked, they sang; trying to hasten the dinner. They knew it would soon come, but all the same they never had anything better to do. Albert was hardly in that. He used to say: 'Unno no call me no Count Tepple.' Maybe that was a name his breddas fastened on to him since he was so stand-offish and loved keeping to his own company. Anyway, all of them were just waiting to hear, 'Come', and they would run with their paki go get it full up of peas soup with corn dumplings or whatever was cooking. Nothing like that naa happen now. Good food naa happen again. It is pure artificial fertiliser they are using nowadays, and through that the food no have any taste.

The only way to get good food now is to plant your own ground. And when you decide where you going to plant, you have to throw down grass, food peelings, cow and horse dung – manure – on that piece of land, then leave the mulching for a time before you work it into the soil to soak right in and replenish the earth. Leaving the land to rest is just common sense; while this portion is out of production, you plant over *deh-so*, and you rotate the crops you're growing. This is no hurry-come-bring-up something. For a start, if you abuse the land, it will abuse you right back. The old people would also make a natural fertiliser by gathering certain kinds of wood and stone and burning them right down to form a white powder called white-lime, which had many uses; as fertiliser or for preserving ground food, yam and such like for a good portion of time. Whenever you set down fertiliser, you don't plant straight away; you must leave it for rain to fall on, or else throw water 'pon it, then leave it fallow for a time before you do any cultivation. It would surprise you the amount of yam, gungoo peas, sweet potato – man, wholesome vegetation – that comes up after you bother *tek* time and plant your ground with care.

Samson

My Uncle Sam was married to a woman named Mimi Taylor from Aintree. I have the juice to give you about Uncle Sam. Him did strong, you know; fi-him strength! Man, Maama used to say Sam was so strong him one could-a clean lift up the house. She told us how him one would carry three tins of sugar go a Newmarket. Three big tins, one time! You know kerosene pan? That is how big the sugar pans he carried did stay. That time Sam was strong so till it come in supernatural. Me seh! Other men used donkeys or walked with one tin in their hand or else balanced on their shoulder, but Sam managed three tins one time; one pan on his head and two in his hands. Sometimes, it was four tins him did have – don't ask me how he managed them. He came in like Samson from the Old Testament. And just like the Bible character, they say from he was born, his hair was never cut and they used to tell us how everybody use to have it for joke whenever Maama and the other women called Sam to plait his hair, for he was quite a humorous character and because he had such pretty hair, it was every woman's delight to comb it. And this time, while they were combing it, he would be giving them jokes, they would be giving him jokes, joke a give joke , and so it went on. You could just imagine.

When they plaited his hair, it was pretty and long so till any self-respecting young girl could feel envious. They would just plait it, wrap it round and round his head and pin it up, then put on his cap. But what happened was, bad-minded people cut off Uncle Sam's hair. Everybody outside the family was just wondering, 'wait, what kind of man is dis mek him one a-carry so much sugar one time?' And him never have no donkey or nothing, just walk him walking all the way to market. So, some covetous people started wondering where Uncle Sam's strength came from. They bribed some *fifth-columnists* from inside family circle – and that was how they got to find out that Uncle Sam's hair was not to be cut. Now, one time Sam did a go a' Newmarket. In those days, you used to have to pay to go inna market. So, this particular occasion, Uncle Sam paid, went in, found his spot and put down his sugar pans and then went back out to collect something. When he came back, the gateman said he had to pay to go back in. Sam told him that he paid already and put his sugar down inside. That caused contention and the police arrested him. Maama said two policemen couldn't manage him; it took four of them to hold him down. They beat him so till him was black and blue; all inna him face. And, through he was red-skin, you know, every bruise showed and his hands, face, everywhere swelled up.

Those bad-minded people who knew the secret had set him up and made the police hold Sam down and cut off his hair. After that, all him strength was gaan. Clean gaan. He never had any power again; even *mus-mus* or the youngest baby could lead him anywhere for how he became meek as a lamb. It come in like the story of Samson and Delilah.

When we a did pickney, Uncle Sam would always siddung and tell us that story. Any time I went to look for my uncles, they would always leave food covered up for me, especially Albert; he would have his *bimbye* ready so we could eat together. And whenever I was going to Kilmarnoch, I would stop round there and get some *mouth-water* and some ole-time stories before continuing the journey. Those stories would set my little imagination afire; stories like the hunting of the wild hog (to tell the truth, I did always love any kind of story that had anything to do with food), or David and Goliath or Daniel in the lion's den from the Bible. When we used to hear those Bible stories next to the stories about my uncles, like the one about the astounding strength of Uncle Sam, we could never see any difference; they were just as awe-inspiring as one another.

Aunt Martha

I had an aunt named Martha Scarlett. How she could sing; she come in like bell own self! But she only had one leg and used to walk with a peg. We pickney used to siddung and get the story about how Aunt Martha came to lose her leg and how all through '*sake-a grudgefulness*', wicked people *obeah* poor Aunt Martha.

When she was a girl, Martha was best friends with a girl named Ninel. Martha had what we would call a trebello voice or soprano; whenever she would sing and hit a high note her voice would ring like a bell. She always used to get encores and people would fan her and they even used to pay her to sing.

Martha and Ninel were bosom friends; if Martha no eat potato, no bother give Ninel potato. If one wear a certain frock, the other one had to wear the same thing; two closer friends you could never find. Ninel used to speechify, and people would praise her whenever she recited poetry or Bible passages. Ninel could render grown men to muteness with her eloquence:

> The quality of mercy is not strain'd,
> It droppeth as the gentle rain from heaven
> Upon the place beneath. It is twice blest;
> It blesseth him that gives and him that takes.

But, Martha could cause eye-water to fall with a spiritual song like:

> Take up thy cross, the Saviour said,
> If thou wouldst my disciple be;
> Deny thyself, the world forsake,
> And humbly follow after me.

Even if she did sing a wordly song, it could not fail to pull every heart-string:

> Drink to me only with thine eyes,
> And I will pledge with mine;
> Or leave a kiss but in the cup,
> And I'll not look for wine.
> The thirst that from the soul doth rise
> Doth ask a drink divine;
> But might I of Jove's nectar sup,
> I would not change for thine.

The two of them, Martha and Ninel, were the best in *fi-dem* gift, whether in school or in church.

Now, Ninel grudged Martha because everybody did love her voice and considered her talent to be without any equal. Eventually, Ninel go tell her madda, Inez Woodley, seh Martha get more praises than she. She coveted her even though she was getting praise for giving good recitations. Ninel still felt that Martha's position was better than her own. Inez Woodley took what her daughter said to heart and she went and prepared black magic to set against Martha. She gave Ninel the preparation and told her how to set it up. Inez Woodley instructed Ninel to put the article between two posts where she knew Martha was going to walk, but she told Ninel to make sure Martha walked in front of her and what again she was to do to apply the bait. *Mek no mistake, is obeah we talking about.*

So, that Saturday, Martha and Ninel a go a market. When they reached the certain posts, hear Ninel, 'Go on before me Mart.' Martha went ahead of her and as she did so, she *buck* her shin.

Ninel said: 'What do yu, Mart?'

Hear Ninel, 'No mind, Mart. It wi' soon better.'

Notice is three times Ninel call Martha's name; that was all part of the set up. So as they're going on, deep in conversation about what dem a go wear to the concert the next day. Remember dem is bosom friends; if one wear black, the other also have to wear black. Not even twins were as close as those two.

So, this particular day, the pair were going a market go sell Naseberrys and Sweet Sops. So, Ninel set the thing her mother gave her, and Martha is none the wiser. When they reached a certain area, they met a river or pond, so they had to cross over in a canoe. By this time Martha said she wasn't feeling too good, and by the time they arrived at the market, she was roasting with fever. At the market, Ninel did the trading; selling off fi-her goods and fi Martha's because, by now, Martha really took sick. Even the bruised fruit that no usually sell, the market people bought them on account of how they liked Martha. They could use that to feed the animals, you see. Ninel put the money in a *two foot thread bag* and after that she went round to buy everything that she and Martha did need in the market.

Come the end of the day, they packed up dem load and made ready to go home. By this time now Martha have ague; she did just a-roast with fever. Ninel all go buy bay rum to rub her down and inhale when she got home. *Mek me tell yu, friends good, but is not all kinds of friends yu fi keep.*

The next day, Sunday, is the concert. Martha did still sick but she decided she a go sing anyway. Like every other time before, the people loved her and showed dem appreciation by standing up, fanning her and bawling for encore. Sick as she was, few would believe that Martha's singing voice wasn't an angel's. But when she reached home after the concert, she nearly collapsed from the fever. They noticed a little pimple 'pon her foot but it never hurt her so nobody worried about it. However, by now a strange kind of sickness was beginning to take root.

Little after that, Martha began to get worse. Her foot started to break out in all manner of sores and when it really took bad, all kinds of sea creatures and slime would come out of it; creatures like *sea puss* and *sea conk*, and mucus would just seep out of her foot! Whenever it took her, she just had to cry out in pain. Whatever that evil woman used to mek the *derek* that was what was coming out Martha's foot. Aunt Martha couldn't eat any kind of fish whatsoever from that started. But whenever the foot would break out in sores, afterwards it would just heal right up and close up like a little button-hole. To look at it, you wouldn't know anything was wrong, but after a certain time the whole thing would just bruk out again. They used to have to wash the foot with *bluestone water* and rub her foot with *horsefitititia*, which is the same thing they tek rub 'pon young baby head when dem born to mek sure the child no ketch cold. They even tried all kinds of home remedies to treat the condition, and by the time dem think to tek her to see a *madda woman* it was too late, the sickness had gone too bad. People seh it would have been better if they did take Martha's singing voice rather than do that to her foot.

Anyway, years later when Martha was a grown woman, Inez Woodley took sick and was on-dying. She sent for Martha, telling her 'come quick'. When Martha went, Inez told her to let her see the foot. Now, Inez's voice did shake and quake like a goat (rub your throat with your hand while you're talking and you can get a reflection of her din).

Hear her, 'Lawd, a dat me bring meself to.'

Martha said, 'What yu do Auntie Inez?'

Inez said, 'Every day Ninel would come and tell me how people praise yu more than she, so me mek her *puddung* de someting fi harm yu.'

Martha asked her, 'Den a dat mek yu do it Auntie Inez?'

All Inez could say on her death-bed was, 'A dis me come to.'

A couple days later when Inez Woodley died there was no Bible reading and no burial songs because the people all said she was too wicked. They grabbed the Bible from the parson and said, 'Not a Bible reading a read.'

Is pure bad wud and cussing they used to bury that woman. They even buried Inez Woodley head way down and when they finished, they built a *fire-roll* 'pon top of the grave and cried out, 'Mek de brute burn inna hell!'

Martha went to the funeral, but she didn't take part in all that carry on.

Later on, things got so bad with her leg that they had to cut it off at the knee and give her a wooden foot, or peg-leg. She had to put the knuckle on a little soft pillow and tie the cord around her waist to hold it in place. Whenever she was walking you would hear, 'ku-ku kum-kum, ku ku kum-kum'. But she could still beat anybody in a race, and if you thought you were bad, make fun of her peg-leg to let her hear you! You would find out. But Martha's singing voice was as matchless as ever.

Aunt Martha never married and she never had any pickney, but she became '*a joyful mother of children*'.

When she died, they wanted to bury the peg-leg with her, but decided to keep it to help somebody else.

After we listened to the story of Aunt Martha, we always used to get a warning about watching out for bad-minded people. Our elders used to chide us to, 'Mind yu friends and company because is dem know yu secrets and if yu bad-luckied, is dem same one will reveal it.'

2
Highdays and Holidays

Picnic

Round about August time they used to have picnics and, most often, Maas Nat would be the gateman.

Picnic day was something special; it would come in like sports day combined wid harvest festival. All kinds of merry-making would go on. You had to pay to go in and people would be all about selling goods: straw hats, playthings, grater cake, fried fish and *bammy*, balloon, clappers, starlight, peanuts, candy, *jerk* pork, all manner of good things. Church brethren and sistren would turn up from all over yonder on foot, horse-back or in buggies that looked like wagons, with everybody piled up on top singing and enjoying themselves on the journey. Sometimes, if a gal and bwoy were looking to court, they would try to get their chance at the picnic, although keeping away from inquisitive on-lookers wasn't easy. In those days, from a girl was talking with a young fellow, everybody had them as good as married!

I remember one picnic me did go to with Ole Jane. Everybody sang songs until dem did hoarse, run up and dung in races till dem was weary. I must have had three dips inside Missa Headley's grab bag but I never win anything splendid. And to this day, I can still hear the fife and drum playing as the band marched around the church grounds. They even had mule races and we all played games and ate till the food was clean done, but a picnic – or 'pitnit' as some people used to say – was never complete without some story-telling, songs, jokes and riddles, when the leading story-tellers used to say:

> 'Riggle me riggle, riggle me ree
> riggle me dis riggle or perhaps not!'

Cuthbert Grandison was the chief riddler.
Hear him, 'Who am I? Me an' yu come out we mumma belly same

time and any which part yu a go, me is always before or never far past; sometimes yu see me, sometimes not, but we will always be together as long as life shall last. Who am I?'

Some guessed 'twin', while some said 'guardian angel', or even 'familiar spirit', and when we guess come and guess go, eventually somebody shouted out correctly, 'shadow!', and so that person got to give a riddle, and so on.

Now, after the picnic finished, everybody cleared up and whoever was able would rush home to bathe or clean up ready for more enjoyment. What used to happen is, when the day-time merriment was over, they used to hold dances in the early evening. They would make a 'bourd' which came in like a simple, erect house made out of long poles and thatched over with coconut thrash, only the doorway was left open.

This one time me did well *waan'* go to the dance, and for the whole day me did look forward to it. And so the time came and while we were going along, we heard a big commotion up ahead. All you could see was rock stones a-fling, bottles a-fly. *A mussi did rum fight*; that's the way it always turned out when the people were drinking rum. Sometimes, from some of those man just smelled the liquor, they were intoxicated. And, more often than not, all you know is a fight would soon follow.

Ole Jane said, 'Come, Emel, come!' and we turned round and went straight back home. When we reached the yard, David, my bredda said, 'Come, dem cool down now, mek we go back.'

I told him, 'Me? Not dem two foot yah!' Old Jane said she naa go back either so we stayed home and heard them start up the music again and listened to the people enjoying themselves with the heap of laughing and *gerrey*. We never heard any more *bad wud* or arguments after that till way up in the night when all the merry-making ceased and everybody went home to sleep off the long day. Who no ketch home, slept same place round the bourd. Sometimes, as part of the celebrations, they would hold cock fights, and those big men would just drink rum and gamble their lives away as those cocks would claw out one another's flesh until you could smell the rawness of blood mingling with the sourness of wet fowl feathers; while the unholy and seductive essence of rum and tobacco smoke danced together heavy in the air.

But I never used to go a dance often. Sometimes I would just stand up to one side and see how the people did a dance; see how 'dem throw dem foot'. Me mah? I was too shy and never used to dance except a-yard. When the old people were not about we used to dance in the house, but no vulgar dances; no whiney-whiney, only quadrille, mento and such like.

They had a saying: 'dance a-yard before yu dance abroad'. When I was growing up, I know for sure that I did plenty dancing a-yard, but me no remember if me did ever dance abroad any at all.

Some of the old time people had the notion that dancing was a sin and if their pickney ever danced, it would bar they themselves from going to heaven, so most of my generation couldn't *tek fast* go dance and let the old people see, for that was the way of the devil, so they believed. And, furthermore, if you did think yourself bad, you dare pucker up your mouth and whistle. Whistling came in like another cardinal sin if you were a child, and especially a 'girl-chile'. To those ancient minds, a whistling woman was like a laying rooster or a crowing hen!

Hussay

I remember a festival the Indians used to keep, the hussay – or 'who-seh'. We came to call it 'coolie hussay'. It was a ceremony where the Indian people used to march and sing songs, cook rice and other special kinds of food, and dress up in bright, colourful garments made out of delicate kinds of claat, like silk. The women and gal-pickney dem used to wear plenty silver bangles, necklaces, earrings and even noserings, beads and some had a painted mark in their forehead; very jolly. The older ones especially did have their heads covered, the men wearing turbans, which we used to call 'coolie-wrapper', while the women's head-covering was a red claat, which we called 'coolie red'. But while some of the men did look smart and dressed like ordinary Jamaicans, some of them used to wear jengey-jengey – bedraggled-looking clothes. Some did have their machete in hand, others a long stick, while some were beating a drum or blowing a *fee-fee* while the women played the timbrel. The hussay was a duppy festival and the coolies all came together from all over to enjoy their special time.

Me madda, Ole Jane, was friendly with a coolie lady named Shabna who lived with her husband Rahman over Strathbogie. We used to exchange goods and their children, Aisha, Ram and Sukrie, used to play with me and my brothers and sisters from time to time when we were passing those parts. The whole community of them would look forward to the festival, which Shabna's father would help organise every year. That old man would sit down quietly, barely a word passing his lips, shy to kill even a mosquito, and scrape the bamboo canes he was intending on using. As the new moon was approaching, you would see more and more of them getting involved and by then the old man had set up the frame, undergone most of the preparation. They fixed up the wooden ornament, tall as a house, but light through it was made out of bamboo, and took time painting it over and covering the whole thing with flowers and a whole manner of bright paper and ribbons. When it was ready, they carried it on some long poles; two men a front, two behind. It was something to behold.

As me seh, is duppy festival, and inside they put two small coffins, for the hussay was to commemorate two brothers, Hassan and Hussein, who did war against one-another because they did both want power and in the battle, the two of them died same time, Shabna told me. From that, the Indians set out to hold a memorial when they would mek the hussay and pray to fi-dem god for prosperity, call up the spirits of ancestors (me never like to hear that part, for that is calling up duppies). Further to that, they would make a sacrifice, hold a feast and all manner of celebrations for the whole day.

If I remember rightly it was around March time they did have the festival, but it was always on the ninth night after the new moon – same like we would hold *Nine Night* for our dead. When time they were ready, four men would carry the monument and while they were marching with the hussay in front, all the people would sing and dance. First of all they sounded like they were mourning, the women wailing inna fi-dem tongue, and afterwards they started singing, 'hu-say, hu-say,' and beating that drum, 'bom-bo-bom-bo-bom,' blowing the fee-fee whistle, shaking their rattle and knocking the timbrel. They would carry the monument, marching and singing, with all manner of people following on behind looking in awe at the spectacle, to a certain area where everybody would join in the feasting; eating roti, laddoo, khurma, rice curry, cakes, candy and many enjoyable things. The celebration would come in like fi-we picnic, with games, dancing and laughter. There was a fire-eater and different magic tricksters where a man could make ribbons come from anywhere, even out of people's ears, or make money vanish. Some of the young men did have a special kind of dance where they used sticks; waving them and clashing with another man's like in a fight, and throwing the sticks in the air, *turning-dem-roll* and catching them, quick. How those people could enjoy themselves, and what a noise! Only they never used to handle rum or any strong drink for the festival. Bimeby, it was evening time, and once more the men would pick up the monument and the singing would start afresh as they marched off in the direction of the sea or a river. When they reached the seashore or river-side, they would offer up prayers and throw the hussay in the water, and it would wash right out of sight. This time now, the sun did a dip inna sea, so the hussay would drift far out into the sunset. But them never finish yet, for a portion of them would stay same place singing, dancing, eating and carrying on the festivities right up into the night; all the gathering of people singing fi-dem songs and making their own parade. You might not know what they were saying or what was the significance, but all the same yu could spectate and appreciate that it was their own culture. In-spite of all obstacles, they still managed to keep their tradition going strong.

Jon-kannu

Jon-kannu – or John Canoe – as some people call it, now, that was our masquerade. It was a festival to look forward to. Come end of year, at Christmas time, everybody's skin would ketch a-fire to go look 'pon Jon-kannu. Later on some church people use to try discourage it, seh a no good something and talk about how the people were carrying on too wild and vulgar, but who wanted to go would still attend and enjoy themselves quite well. As a little pickney, the first time yu go a Jon-kannu yu have so much to see and so much excitement that it come in like a dream yu a-dream. People from the district or a next area would dress up in a variety of different costumes and put on a performance; dancing, playing instruments, telling jokes and singing. One of the dancers did have on a big cow head and cow tail – how real it looked! Some of those entertainers did feava duppy, and it was easy for we children to be afraid, especially when we saw the devil with his long fork, devil tail and two horns sticking up out of him head. It would even come in like him did have fire in his eyes, and how he would rush amongst the crowd frightening people. Nuff pickney would hold on tight to their mother's hand and even start bawling when they saw the devil – or 'debil', as we say. Another dancer did have a whip and went round the place beating all who took his fancy, and wan next one did have on a pretty suit of clothes with something siddung 'pon him head come in like boat. A next performer was the doctor, another a skeleton. One was horse head, galloping about clapping people with his teeth, while smady else did come in like a jockey. This time who didn't have on a mask had their face painted, all some men dressed up like women, though as children you were not to know; you would believe it was some pretty, pretty women you were seeing. People used to throw money or give the pickney dem the money to fling to the dancers, while the one with the whip especially would rush to grab up the coins. As it would happen, people used to pay up so that the man with the whip wouldn't lick them – although it was only 'play him did a-play'. Still, saying that, it was common knowledge that if a person in the Jon-kannu did have a grievance with smady, he could wait till masquerade and extract his vengeance. How that would go? That character would dress up in the carnival, flashing a whip or wielding a machete, or clapping the teeth of the horse head, move on to single out the person him was in a grievance with so as to cut them or whip them hard.

Since it was masquerade, he could then form excuse that it was accidental. Some people no easy. But, oh, what a carry on! There was dancing, music, drumming: 'dum-ti-dum-ti-ti dum, dum-ti-dum-ti-ti dum,' way into the night, and food a-plenty, excitement everywhere at Jon-kannu. I remember Monkey, Pitchy-Patchy, Jack, King and Queen, Actor Bwoy, Horse Head, Indian Girl – who would believe that was a man dressed up like woman, with that long silky hair, looking glass, push-up bosom and big backside, and those red, red lips? But it was that devil! Man, him did come in fearful and if you never mind sharp you would believe it was truly the devil.

Note
(From *Smith's Voyage to Guinea 1727* in *The Annals of Jamaica*, Bridges, 1828):
'The court of the ruined Prussian fort of Fredericksbourg Castle was paved by the Kabaschir Negro, John Conny, whose castle and deeds of barbarous valour are still commemorated by certain tribes in Jamaica at the Christmas festival.' Since Conny 'used skulls, bone souvenirs from his cannibal feasts to decorate state appartments and buildings', so the Prussians used John Conny's remains to 'pave their castle'.

3
The Learning Tree

Labour for learning before you grow old
For learning is better than silver and gold
Silver and gold will vanish away
But a good education will never decay

School days

As pickney we used to go a-school out at Salem next to the old church-house.

We always had to rise up early-early when dew-water was still on the ground and the air was sharp and chill. Clock? We never had none o' that! Only, before you go sleep a night-time, you would set your mind that at such and such time you must wake up and so it would go. Or, you would listen out for the cock's crowing, when they say, 'cock a bawl fi dem drawers'; on the first crow or second; whichever one was your alarm.

But some children would listen out instead to hear pears dropping if it was the right season. Those avocado pears we called 'puss prayers' through how cats have a reputation for loving them and some would even sit under the pear tree 'a-pray' for them to drop off.

When those pears were ripe they would drop, 'bom!' with a heavy thud on the ground, especially in the early morning, and as soon as you heard the sound you would get up and run quickly to collect them in your frock tail, apron or in a *crocus bag* before anybody else. At other times if puss was in the area yu would see them just tucking in, all when the pear was ripe till it rotten.

Even when we were going a-school, you know, there was a whole heap of housework to do before class started. That's why we had to rise up early; so many things to do; water fi go fetch with a big pudding pan on your head, walking to where the waterpan, well or river was, and not just one trip mind you, sometimes three, four, and if it was you alone doing it for the family then you can just imagine.

First thing every morning, Maama would clean out her fire-hearth; sweep out the ashes, and take water to wash it out thoroughly. And if there wasn't enough wood, you or your siblings would have to go gather some so she could catch up her fire to mek breakfast – '*chaklata*'. She might decide to put in couple breadfruits to roast along wid a sweet potato or yam fi the ole man tek wid him to work. Meanwhile, Papa might have been tending to the animals and you would have to help feed the chickens and collect their eggs, or else milk the goats. Maama, or another one of the big people, usually milked the cows.

All the minor work used to be shared out amongst the youngsters; the bigger ones would get the most and the younger ones would get whatever dem could manage; but one thing, idleness never lived inna fi-we yard, not-at-all. Everybody had something to do and was responsible for helping to get everyting in order. From daylight to dusk that was the way it was.

After that first set of errands, Maama would comb our hair; plait it, or the older pickney dem would comb fi the younger ones. But, before we could put our minds to school, we would have to carry several bundles o' cane to Maas Nat's sugar mill. He used to mek sugar and sell it in big tins, even molasses and 'ginger sugar' which was a popular candy at the time.

We never had just one set of cane to carry, O! We would-a carry cane till Maas Nat said, 'Leave de balance till unno come from school.'

Then we would do the same thing again when school was over. It was hard work, but one incentive was that we used to get our own sugar pan full o' sugar and Papa would always mek sure we got some of the *copper wash* to drink, which was so delightful.

When we finished in the morning, we would eat, say, banana porridge and *johnny-cakes*, and drink some cocoa-tea, coffee or cane-liquor before we would have to run off to catch a' school. Or else, we might have got a piece of St. Vincent roast yam, wid roasted salt-fish and some bush tea for our breakfast. This time, if we were having to hurry, we would be blowing on the food while we're eating through how it hot!

Sometimes, as the last of the food hit our belly, we would get up, wash out our mouths and our vessels, that would be a paki or china plate, and run off wid our lunch-pan to mek sure we were not late for school. Oftentimes we would get beaten with a tambrind switch or belt if we were late.

We would all line up outside the school house, each with our own class, and, like soldiers on parade, be inspected; slate and chalk in one hand, lunch pan in the other; eyes front; body erect and to full attention; some wearing shoes, some in dem *ten commandments*.

'Good mawning, school', said the teacher.

'Good mawning, (sir or mam), good mawning every one,' we would chorus with one healthy voice. Then we would say prayers, sing a song and say the school pledge. The latecomers or stragglers would be made to stand up a' back till everybody had marched inside to begin class, then they would face judgement and be made to give account for their tardiness.

Whosoever didn't carry a lunch-pan would take a yam, breadfruit, sweet-potato or some other food-kind which would be cooked up together in a common pot, along with some *salt-ting* for the school meal. Looking back it was a good custom and nobody was left out, but we always used to carry fi-we own food for the recess.

One thing, we grew up knowing that eating from people was like a law we were not to break, and that even extended as far as the school meal. And more besides, the school meal came in like a form of charity and nobody really wanted to admit they was so destitute; you know, when people are poor, pride can be one thing, sometimes the only thing, they have of any currency.

One time me and Alice, my sister, did a-run go a-school and Alice saw one dutty big snake in the road ahead. She took 'fraid, but me did just bend dung and pick up a rockstone; Pam!, me ketch the brute, lick out him gut-hole. Me did too licky man, me naa'nah miss.

It coiled up wounded but me grabbed some more rockstones and just finished him off. A little while after, you were bound to see *jon-crows* on the scene. A story goes that when *jon-crows* are gathered together around a carcass, they dare not touch it until the Headman Jon-crow, a white, controlling bird, arrives. When him come, him start by walking round the body two or three times. Then he says to the other crows, 'What kill dis man?'

The others would chorus all together, 'Fat!'

The headman then would simply take out the eye – that is all him want – and fly off with it. After that, the others could devour the flesh, but not a minute sooner.

Love weeds

Most other mornings on the way to school, if we were not in such a hurry, we would make 'love weeds'. We would gather certain wild flowers and wisses together in a bundle and form it into a *cotta*. When we finished, we would put it down by the roadside for the person we loved.

After a certain time, if the 'love weeds' started to grow, it meant that the person loved you in return. If not, then the person didn't love you. Those 'love weeds' were the kind of plants that would grow like a creeper; before long it would be growing all over, stretching itself right out.

I always used to set them for my school friends, especially Margie Taylor who was my best friend.

Beating

On the way to school, while we a mek-haste; running and walking fast – for is miles we going – we would stop on the journey and pick a leaf from a Leaf-of-Life bush, spit on it and throw it up in the air. If it landed on top, that meant we were going to be early, but if it landed on its bottom, we would-a late. If it looked like we be late, we would pick some 'Cow-Itch Leaf'. This was a plant that really scratched the skin, but what you did was to pick it and rub it in the palms of your hands so if you were going to get beaten it wouldn't *hot* too much.

Or else, some pickney would pick up a handful of stones and throw them behind their back, taking care not to look behind. Others still had a practice of putting a few stones tied up inside a posy of wildflowers given to the teacher, as ways of averting any beating or other hostile treatment. If punishment was due, 'luck' would change dem mind, so we believed.

Beating was a common practice, and some teachers really took it for relish, especially one we did call 'Teacher Fi-Licking', a violent brute named Maas Edwin Thompson, who used to soak a belt in water to chastise errant pickney with. He named the belt, Miss Berry, and whenever him was wielding it – grabbing that youngster tight and lashing into the bare backside – him would chorus, 'Yes, Miss Berry a go mek yu merry!' If doling out licks was not his passion, I would say it was his joy; for how he would wield the whip until the welts rose like lizards on those tender flesh, while Teacher Fi-Licking's red eyes bulged and his sweating forehead dripped. If he missed a stroke, he had a habit of lashing wildly with buckle and all. If it wasn't a belt, we could expect a guava or tambrind switch as 'rod of correction'. So, avoiding lateness was of paramount importance during my school days.

Sometimes my school friend Edith Brown would call fi me. She lived clear over Thicket Bottom, a long way off from anywhere. At that time we lived over Briscoe. If I did ever ketch round to Thatch Valley and no see Edith, me would haffi run like hell because me was certain to be late; at those times, me would have to run till me wheeze. Back at that time me used to suffer a little with asthma, although I outgrew it later on. On those days when I missed Edith, and when you looked up and saw the full sun flaming high up in the sky like a marvellous sour orange, I'd know for sure I was late. One time me did get beaten a-school, but not through lateness.

What happened was that I did have a teacher named Miss Carrie Stewart who was quite a disciplinarian. This particular day, we were inside the lesson and she went outside to talk to *smady*, so she told the class to be quiet till she returned. When she came back in she asked who was talking.

She said: 'Unno get on so miserable. Who was mekking so much noise?'

Everyone else was talking and playing, while I was quiet as can be.

But one li' pulp y'eye gal who never liked me, through me was brighter than she, told the teacher I was the one responsible. The gal was always asking me to help her with her work, but through me refuse she go frame me. My friends told Teacher Stewart say a no true but she wouldn't listen; instead she sent for a tambrind switch to beat me with.

That Miss Carrie Stewart beat me till me arm bleed and there was blood on my white school blouse.

When I reached home after school, Maas Nat saw the blood and I had to tell him what happened. He carried me up to Teacher Stewart's house round at Wesley Park. When we got there the ole man cried out, 'hold daag', to let dem know someone was approaching the yard, so the dogs wouldn't attack.

Teacher Carrie was there with her husband, Elik Stewart, who was a teacher too. Maas Nat ask Miss Carrie why she beat me till me bleed. Hear she come ask me if she did really beat me and what it was she did use. *This time now the bitch well and know what she do, yu know.* Me tell her 'yes, you was responsible' and me look clear in her eye. There was no denying it.

Her husband told her she was wrong to take another child's word against mine and beat me till she drew blood. He said if she beat me, she should have beaten the whole class. So, Missa Elik Stewart sent me to go see his son Ernie who was a doctor, to make him take care of the cut. If Maas Nat wasn't satisfied with how things had turned out, he would have taken it further, but through Miss Carrie submitted and said sorry, he left it there.

After that, them other pickney at school were just killing themselves, hurrying to be on time, but no matter how it did late, I just took my time because me know seh me naa get no more beating again!

But to this day me still have the mark on me shoulder where Teacher Stewart took a tambrind switch and beat me.

Jack-fruit knee

Talking about marks, you know I have a knee which *feava jack-fruit*! The *knee-cup* is very big and stands out from the other one, but it's not so me was born. The story goes that while I was still in my youth, one Friday I was ironing clothes, getting ready to go a market the next day.

When me done iron, me go wash a next set of clothes. Now, me never bother wait to cool off after me iron before me go do the washing. Alright. Next day now, me go a market as arranged and the sun was hot so till me sweat, yu see! Then all upon a sudden it began to drizzle as *devil and him wife start fight* and very soon a heavy rain started falling. Me run go shelter in the orange grove, but when it started coming down heavily, me and couple others run go tek refuge under backra house. So we were under there, dry as can be, watching the rain; and hearing the plinking-plinking sound of rainwater bouncing off the zinc roof and the plecking-plopping whosh of it into gathering water pails; and telling stories and giving jokes. The next thing me know, me started to shiver. By the time the rain stopped and me go home, me never feel good at all. Soon me did just a-shake and a terrible fever started. If you were bad-lucky enough to get caught in a downpour, especially in your bare-feet, that's what you had to expect. Shoes? Yu mussi a-idiat! What we business with shoes in dem days? Certainly, we had our shoes put down for church and other special occasions, but country people more-be-less were often barefooted.

Anyway, me go lie down and Ole Jane brought me some beef soup with a whole heap of pepper to help me sweat out the fever. The next morning, me sick so till. Dem carry me go a Ernie Stewart, the doctor, and him say 'is through me iron and then wash and later go ketch up inna the rain, mek me tek sick'. But he said me constitution was strong and he gave me some medicine.

By Tuesday it was getting worse, but me couldn't go back a doctor so they sent and called the doctor to come look for me. Doctor Stewart used to have to pass fi-we yard to go to him office, so dem mussi go meet him that morning and told him about my condition.

This time me look like when yu lick fowl and it lean 'pon one side and deh 'pon limping before it just keel over.

I was walking like an old woman, ben'-up and feeble. Sardie Palmer, one of we neighbours and the mother of my school mate, Joe, brought Doctor Ernie to the house to look for me. When the doctor arrived, he gave me an injection in the knee and called for a basin. They brought a white basin to him and the doctor held my knee over it and made an incision. Blood just started to drip from me knee into the basin like a sacrificial offering; what manner of corruption came out of the knee, dropping into the basin and clotting up like *egg red*.

Sardie Palmer said, 'Miss Emel, dis would-a certain fi kill yu.'

They took the blood and went to bury it in the earth outside the house. That same day Doctor Ernie carried me to Black River Hospital and I was in there for nearly two weeks. Dr Stewart had a ward there too, and most nights he would come look in on me. When the time came to discharge me, he was the one who came to tell me that I could go home. He did have an assistant named Sidney who carried me back home in the doctor's buggy. That same morning, we left the hospital so early that when we were going along we saw all variety of people just leaving their yard to go a Whitehouse market.

Back at home, I still had to get plenty of rest and my bredda David did carry me go a seaside couple times to get sea-bath. But later on as the years went by, the knee bone just swelled right up like jack-fruit and I had to sit in the sun to help ease the pain. Even now, when the weather starts to get cold, man, this same knee gives me the juice!

Speakey-spokey

We were fortunate to have the chance to go a-school. Some other pickney fi-we age never got to go because they did have to work on the land growing provisions to go sell a-market. Some others couldn't go a school because they were minding baby or working out as maid-servants or 'helpers' for rich people in town, or toiling as labourers in the cane-fields.

Back in those days, getting pickney to go a school was a certain way the parochial authorities used to try and make sure we would keep out of trouble. They never wanted to see bands of youths, especially the boy-pickney dem, roaming up and down the place causing trouble and breeding the girl-children.

Most of the time you would already know your teacher, for they might have been the very one teaching you at Sunday School.

The school itself was just one room, for it was all-age school we were going, so the younger children would sit in front whilst the older ones sat at the back. But, you know, age never mattered too much, for you would have some young pickney who were brighter than their older kin, and all sometimes it was only the younger ones who got to go to school all the time, for their siblings might have had to help out a-yard and only got to attend school once in a blue moon.

It wasn't unusual to have a child who could read and write quite well having parents who never knew '*A from Bullfoot*'. Sometimes, whenever those illiterate folks found themself in a situation where they had to read, they would simply tell you that dem 'can't see' and run call a pickney to read for dem.

In class, whatever teacher wrote on the blackboard, you would learn it by rote, recite it over and over again until it sank into your *coco*. After that, you would write it out on your slate, then learn it overnight and be prepared to stand up in class and recite it before everybody.

In those days teachers never made fun to beat you in your hands or on your backside if you were slow to learn, or if you misbehaved in class. And, you know, some of the biggest problems used to happen when there were children who talked the broad, raw patois before a teacher who always tried to make believe they had just come over from England, or, more exactly, a teacher who sounded like dem did have hot food inna dem mouth!

Those teachers used to affect the speech of blue-bloodied English aristocrats! *Speakey-spokey* we called them. And they would always make it their point of business to pick on those badly spoken children and try to disgrace them in front of their classmates. It came in like those teachers were trying to shame us because we were poor, black, country pickney, and the only reason for them to do that was because they were ashamed to be poor and black country people themselves.

Learning by rote wasn't such a bad thing; from you committed something to memory, you would find it would stay in your head your whole life sometimes. Early on we learned the 'Our Father' prayer and Psalm 23, 'The Lord is my Shepherd'. We also learned certain dates in history and parts of the world, and the school pledge: 'I pledge myself to remember that at all times and in all places I am my school's representative. May nothing I do or say in either word or deed ever bring disgrace upon it.' And we had 'Memory Gems' to learn, such as:

> 'Any coward can fight a battle when he's sure he can win;
> but give me the man who has the pluck to fight when he's
> sure of losing.'

And how did we remember the three counties of Jamaica? 'Cornmeal, Mix-it-up and Stir-it'!; that is to say, Cornwall, Middlesex and Surrey. But most of all we learned about England's Kings and Queens, the British Empire and about Christopher Columbus. We had a song about Columbus, but we couldn't sing it let teacher hear. I don't remember the whole thing,

> Irish potato grow 'pon tree
> vi va macafat
> Columbus poup a yu!

The children would sing the song while point at themselves and at one another till the final word – a yu! – which would show the culprit who had farted. Now, you couldn't be bold and use the word 'poup' mek older people hear or they would lick out yu marrow. If you ever needed to pass wind, you would, 'cry excuse' and go outside to go 'ease yu body'. As children together farting would always be a source of merriment, but anytime big people were around, it was a serious matter and we didn't dare laugh about it; they were so strict.

Another song I remember singing was about the Titanic, that mighty ship which did sink after they bragged and boasted that Gaad himself couldn't submerge it:

> Some were drinking and a-gambling when
> the Titanic went down
> Some were throwing dice and playing cards
> when the Titanic went down
> what a sinning there was going on
> when the Titanic went down

I also recall what jubilation did go on at the end of The Great War and how we did rejoice over Armistice Day; how we children did wave British flag and enjoyed candy for the first time, even if we didn't fully understand the reason why, war had ended. That was reason enough for feelings of great joy.

At school we were taught nothing but admiration and respect for backra history and backra people. After all, it was they who were providing schools and churches and hospitals, and even building roads, so we really learned to look up to dem and admire dem.

Bull-in-a-pen

Ting-a-ling-a-ling
school bell ring
teacher baggy tie up wid a piece o' string
string pop, baggy drop
ting-a-ling-a-ling!

Recess time at school was quite enjoyable. The bell would ring, 'ting-a-ling-a-ling', and we would line up silently by the door in good order till teacher said we could go outside to play. Afterwards, when the bell rang again, we would do the same to come back inside.

At recess, after you finished eating your mango, sour-sop, star-apple or whatever you carried to *nyam*, the bwoys used to mek and play with their *gigs*, or play marbles, and we girls used to play ring games, or mek dolly babies; corn dollies, and play 'Family' or 'Doctor an' Nurse' underneath the *fancyanna* tree.

Bwoys and girls would rarely play together, although on occasions we might have come together to play a game like 'Bull-in-a-pen' or 'Hide an' seek' or even 'Cashew'. Discipline was something we always learned in school, and if the teacher had cause to beat you, oftentimes you couldn't go home to tell your madda or faada for they might have beaten you too!

On one or two occasions you would find that a child's mumma or puppa would come up the school blowing like a bull ready to beat up the teacher who 'lick dem pickney'. Admittedly though, that situation never happened too often for most parents did truly believe that if their child got beaten, they must have deserved it.

All the same, old time people were too quick to beat-beat, yah *sah*!

Fights

Now, fights were pretty regular. If two pickney clashed in class, they would wait till after school done to fight.

But it couldn't happen outside the school; it would have to be a way off. As they were going along home, they would fling insults at one another; all cuss bad wud and criticise one another's clothes and appearance.

One might say, 'Yu clothes dem feava heng 'pon nail.'

To which the other would reply, 'Eh-heh, well yu nose-hole broad like funnel an' yu foot ben' up like capital 'k'.'

And the other assailant might retort, 'Cho, go kiss jon-crow backside.'

The spectators would have plenty to laugh at, whilst goading on the grudge match.

The enemies even insulted one another's family or brought up ole-time rumours, and, if one o' dem was really bad, spiteful or just plain stupid, him might mention something about the other one's 'mumma'.

Jezan peace! If ever a word could start a fight quickly, it was a word of insult about a next person's mother! Oh, Gaad, that would open fight *said-speed*, and blood would be certain to run as one would strive to bloody the other's nose.

Gals would register contempt by putting an index finger inside dem cheek and slipping it out quick, giving a clucking sound, after which dem would lift up dem frock tail in front of dem enemy; meaning to say, 'kiss my arse' or something worse!

One time Enoch Brown and Cuthbert Hawkins ketch up in a fight down at Bountiful. Dem quarrel come, dem quarrel go. Truth be told it didn't look like the two of them did want to fight at all; by the time school was over they couldn't even remember what the grudge was about, but troublemakers stirred it up so till a fight became like an appointment the two had to keep. So, by the time they reached by Bountiful, the argument looked like it did a linger too long, for neither wanted to throw the first box. One of them said, 'just touch one button 'pon me and yu wi' find out' and the next one repeated the same threat – 'fraid dem 'fraid, you know – but by now it was too late to call off the fight as there were too many spectators about egging on the conflict. Wilfred Anderson, a loud-mouthed fellow, rushed up and just pushed the two of them together to get the fight started.

Aaaii bwoy! It was like when yu go to fry egg and the oil is piping hot. The fighters tore into one another, grappling and *rassling*, even rolling round on the ground battering one another until Pappy Malachi, who was coming along on him horse, stepped in to break it off and admonish the two youths. They were lucky it wasn't a teacher, for if the teachers ever found out about a fight, there would be such a beating, right down to those who stood up watching the confrontation.

All like me, if my mumma or puppa got to know that school finished and me stan' up a-watch fight, dem would lacerate my behind. After you couldn't even stand chatting idly to your school friends. Children had to be very purposeful in those days. For instance, if your madda or auntie sen' you go a shop, they would spit on the ground and tell you, 'No mek it dry before yu reach back.'

But, you know, the two lads Cuthbert and Enoch became firm friends after the fight that day, even into manhood. All in all, the main thing was, going to school gave us a certain amount of confidence; knowing we got a little head knowledge and training in self-discipline. Most children never attended school all the time on account of their responsibilities at home. There were planting days or market days when we were dying to go to school but we had no choice but to *tan a-yard*, mind baby or do ground work.

Who never got the chance to go to school at all missed a wonderful opportunity, although it was only basic education.

Once we finished, the brighter, more good-luckied ones could get a post office job or be trained up to become a basic school teacher, but those chosen few were quite often those youths who were well connected up; who came to school in stockinged feet; and were the teachers' eyeball. Fi-dem people had money and dem skin-colour had pedigree, so every kind of encouragement was considered their birthright.

As for the majority, whether we went to school or not, there was plenty of labour work around. As country people, we never knew it any other way. But going to school was a privilege all the same, and when we outed school we could think about learning a trade.

Out of many, one people?

Apart from church minister and school board, we never really had any direct contact with white people besides some red-red, cashew coloured ones who lived over at Pigeou. We never yet learned that we had a history too, not even about slavery and those other brutalities. If at all, it was for the sake of couple negro spirituals we learned to sing, but for the most part, what we learned was who we were to look up to; the whites – a mussi that mek plenty black people still despise themselves in this world.

It was not till I reached the prime of life that I got to understand certain things about the Africa people, and how we and them are related. All the talk that use to go on in my parents' and grandparents' yard about slavery days and things that happened a long time ago in plantation days, never mattered to me when I was growing up; me would only hear it, but me never did understand. All when Grandma and those other old people used to talk about when dem was 'lickle pickaninny' and how things used to run in the settlement; all some African words they used to say, or when granny talked about 'de guinea people' – those were the Africans that they bring over on vessels – 'the *Guinea neagas*', '*Saltwater neagas*', folks used to call dem. Some of those arrivals would catch hell, for their ways were very peculiar. How she talked it, I learned that down to the very huts that Granny dem use to live in were just like fi the Africa people's own.

You know, they made those huts out of bamboo, covered over with daubing, thatch for the roof, and the owner would leave a place open for the doorway at the front.

Later on I got to understand that the same way we mek fi-we calabash, is same way the Africa people mek fi-dem. The same way we mek mats and rope and padding, is same way dem do it. All like how we beat food in a mortar, pound it down, is same way dem do it.

Granny used to mek *fu-fu* in her mortar. Nowadays, the closest we have to fu-fu, is turn-cornmeal, for Jamaica people naa mek fu-fu again.

As me talking this, me know plain seh plenty *kufenge* no want to hear seh a Africa we come from; it seems they get offended. But what is the offence? Africa is where *neaga* people come from, that is no shame. It is the people who formed slavery and plantation brutality who should feel ashamed. It is the Guinea neaga who sold his own kith and kin who should feel shame. Africa is where our forefathers come from. Yes, we are Jamaicans, but the mumma belly we come out of is Africa same place. Anyway it is hardly surprising we should be ignorant about this, for school was one place that nurtured such thinking; the way they taught us to laud the British Empire, to honorate backra, and to despise our very selves, so quite often a deh-so it set from and got passed on from generation to generation, or as we say, from gingeration to gingeration.

All the same, you have to remember the old saying, *a do fi do mek Guinea neaga come a Jamaica.*

Coolie royal, Chinee royal

The Indians – that is coolies, as they were known – used to mostly live amongst dem one another; keep to themselves, run their own business, speak their own tongue. There was a community of them at Strathbogie and their main concern was growing rice, but plenty of them were labourers working on the big sugar estates run by the backra. Truly they were a set of people who never used to stand around '*a-plait sand and stone breeze*' or a-watch grass grow; they were very hard-working and diligent, not quick to speak or easily provoked. You could always notice them in coolie wrappers and loin-claat, and bright-bright colours. The women had long, pretty hair and most wore many silver bangles and rings on fingers. They kept their own gatherings but sometimes we would mix, especially at festival time on the first day of August when we had picnic and sports day. Oh my! The coolies used to perform some wonderful acts for everybody's enjoyment, some all used to eat fire or juggle swords, it was quite something to behold. Fi-dem conjurers could work all variety of magic tricks, even double money. And they controlled the 'grab bag' which big people and pickney would dip into for prizes. They were a peaceful set of people who took care of kith an' kin, and fi-dem business never used to broadcast all over like fi neaga; they kept their affairs very closely guarded. But quiet as they appeared, coolies were amongst the most awesome obeah workers.

In many ways them and the Chinese were the same. Some might say they were stand-offish, but not all of them were like that. Some did marry and live amongst neaga. And whenever a coolie and a neaga have pickney, people used to call those 'coolie royal', or else 'chinee royal', when a chinee and a black have baby. But not everybody in their community did love it when one of them mixed with our kind in that way. Sometimes they would undergo all kinds of problems from their own people, who might have gone as far as to cut them off for how they hated to see them inter-breeding outside their own race. Contrarily, some black people would be so glad for the chance to mix because then they could boast that fi-dem pickney was 'coolie-royal', and especially if they were mixed with white, they would have a brown baby and to some minds, that would be quite something! To be brown-skin come in like a blessing the way how some people in

Jamaica carry on. True. A no lie. And you would find that brown people used to connect with other brown people, not black, for black come in too low for some of them, or else they would mingle with the handful of whites about the place, if the whites would tolerate them. If a black did get a brown, then from how everybody carried on it would come in like him was good-luckied, and if a black get with a white, man! That black would get raised up, promoted; with his head high and his chest broad, he would feel on top of the world; at last he was somebody, even though the white and brown people never liked to see it a gwaan.

White acting like them was Gaad, brown anxious to be white, some blacks wanting to be anything but black, and every other race satisfied to be anything else except black. See how people funny and after all it is only flesh and blood. All the same, in Jamaica skin colour did come in like it was a form of currency and from you were white, you rich. Any how you were black, you poverty.

4
By de Sweat o' we Brow

Employment

My sister, Florence, was a dressmaker. She used to mek our clothes and me remember some chemise she did fashion. Those dresses would reach down to the calf and had buttons with a high, round collar neck. At other times she would mek dresses with drop waist skirts.

The men used to wear pants which they would belt up or hitch up with *britches* or suspenders over their stripey shirts. Back in those days, poor people used to mek clothes out of all kinds of material, even flour bag. It was just as well, because most times people were working on the land or else doing some other kind of labour-work, so clothes had to be strong and durable.

Who could afford it would have their good clothes put by for special occasions or else would have some piece o' claat put to one side to carry go give the dressmaker or tailor when they were ready for a new garment. We country people might have been poor but we were never dutty yet. Even those who only owned one set of everyday clothes; from you saw them take off those garments, it would be washed and put out to dry, ready to iron and put on again the next day.

Women had a way of dressing that was very particular. At certain times, they would wear a high-necked blouse, delicately frilled, with a long skirt and flowing over-skirt. They would set off the look wid a pretty tie-head; rarely would a lady's head be bare, although for special occasions the hair would be bunched up into two, in a bantu style, or plaited.

Another type of dress was the 'broderie-anglaise' which had a beautiful white blouse fitted around the shoulder, and part of the same material was used to make the over or underskirt. That was for special occasions and the woman would wear some pretty beads around her neck, to complete her graceful appearance.

Another one of my sisters, Alice, also went off to learn the dressmaking trade wid a lady in Savanna-la-Mar and our bredda David took up his apprenticeship as a shoemaker. Another, older bredda had gone to Panama and worked as a gang member on the Panama Canal. The black workers there used to be called 'Silver Employees' and got less payment than the whites who were called 'Gold Employees'. After the canal work, my bredda went and did some cane work in Cuba, banana work in Costa Rica and went back again to Panama, moving from one industry to another, before he came back home to Jamaica. Everybody else in the family went to work out, or to learn a trade; everybody, that is, except me. I stayed a-yard and worked for the family.

Soon after Alice went to work out, Maas Nat got a letter from a young man in her area. He wrote telling our faada how he had met up with his daughter and that he was in love with her. (This time Alice was expecting a baby, but we didn't know.) Maas Nat wrote telling the young man to come so they could discuss the matter. I can't remember what the man's name was, but he was a carpenter by trade and Maas Nat fastened the name 'Jackass Carpenter' 'pon him because he carried on 'just like jackass'. I don't know if a nervous he was nervous making him talk and stammer so, but the name just fastened on him. The poor man used to shake his head like him did have *maggitch*. But him was a nice looking man too, he wasn't coal-black, he was light-skinned and carried himself quite presentable. In the end me no know why he couldn't marry Alice – he must have been married already – but he gave Alice her supportance and everything when the baby was born.

After that incident Old Nat pulled me to one side and said, 'Me hear yu seh you waan' go out to employment. Mark O!, me no say yu no fi go, but if anyting, *no bring it come yah!*'

It's pregnancy him was hinting at, you know, but after that warning, I never mentioned anything more to him again about employment. I was the one who stayed behind.

Work day

On Fridays, most pickney never go a school. They did have to go do ground work 'pon dem people property. I had to do my share of all that; the amount of time I spent working with my father, either helping him on the land or else cooking the big pot full of food to feed the workers whenever there was a digging match.

Certain times of year was planting season, and everybody used to take turns to go and work 'pon one another's land. It would go right round until every piece of ground was cleared and ready for planting or else until everywhere was fully planted up, or ready to harvest. Sometimes, the amount of bush that did have to be chopped down; oftentimes trees had to be felled, hedges needed building and a whole heap of rock-stones had to be cleared off the land, whether it was grass-piece for feeding animals, a cane-piece or ground that was being used for cultivation.

The work gang on the digging match would start off from early in the morning and work right through the day, often till sunset. It was something to see everybody working in harmony; every man had a task to do and you would find him doing it with all his might, no slip-slop. Even women and children used to help out too, maybe weeding grass or doing most of the planting, but the men would always do the heaviest part of the work. My father used to take charge of plenty work days. He could organise well and the way him did know about the land and cultivating, you would think it was one of his relatives.

Those old people knew the land, the seasons and how to cultivate, almost by instinct. What they never knew, wasn't worth knowing.

And they had a respect for the land, too. As we would come to find out, later generations took all that for granted and nowadays don't even want to know about farming. Not so my old man, him and the land were inseparable.

Old Nat used to be a serious kind of man, but every now and then, upon a blue moon, he said or did something that made me know that he had a sense of humour after all. Once in a while he would smoke fish; first salting and then stringing them up over the fire area to smoke. I remember one time as a young girl, I said to him in a little girly voice, 'Bredda Natty, beg yu one a dem *lickle tenkitita*', and with my finger aiming close up by my right eye, me tek time point up to which part the fish were hanging.

Old Nat told me that I never needed to taste any, all I had to do was to 'point' up to which ever of the fish I wanted and say, '*fish ku teeth, teeth ku fish*', and then he would laugh at my bewilderment. Finally, he would pick off one of the fish and give me and I would enjoy it all the more for seeing my ole man happy.

When we were growing up in those days, the old people never used to laugh or give jokes too often, they were very serious, especially when it came to disciplining their children. See, they never made fun to put us 'in our place'; all the while admonishing and quoting scriptures about 'spare not the rod and spoil the child'. But at least we grew up having manners and learning respect for our elders, if not for one another.

Anyway, the digging match was the kind of occasion that brought everybody together in mutual co-operation. Alright, so come the work day, say Wednesday or Friday, we would wake up soon-soon and gathered everything together. In one basket there was peas, cawn (corn), potato slips and yam seed in others, while several other containers were packed out with food that would be cooked later on. Yet another basket had in utensils and the cooking pots. At a certain appointed time, my father would walk round checking everything and when he was satisfied, he would take out his old conch shell and blow it three times to let everybody know we were ready to start off.

As we set off up-a-front, you would just see people coming along from all over to join us. Some had dem hoe and machete or pickaxe 'pon dem shoulder, while the women were loaded up with baskets rested on their heads.

The man whose ground we did a go work on provided a goat to be butchered for the big feed up, and everybody else would bring along hard food; a couple breadfruits, a han' of bananas, some yam, dasheen, co-co or sweet-potato.

So, we would all be going along before sun up; like soldiers marshalling on a mission; the smallest pickney up ahead driving the goat. I always use to ponder how that little kiddy-goat would be skipping along quite well, nibbling a leaf here and there, never knowing his fate.

As we reached where we were going, more often than not it was dense bush, so the men would start to clear a way to let in sunlight; chopping down the over-growth and cutting off branches from trees to let light through, and after that we would set up the cooking area and use the newly-chopped hardwood limbs for fire-wood. On work days, there was never a whole heap of chatting or any arguments at all when my puppa was in charge. Everybody knew what to do, and straight we reach they would set about the job.

As those clearing the bush were going along, another set of fellows followed on behind with pickaxes and digging machetes to root out the bushes and clear away rock stones. The youngsters, including myself, would help roll the boulders and stones over to one set place. Later on those same stones would be used to build a boundary wall or pen. Behind those doing the rooting and clearing, another group of workers would be digging and preparing trenches to drain away rain-water.

Work songs

Before long, plenty work would get done when the men were organised into their gangs; no idle talking, no lazy-bodies, just one purpose; *wuk*. Soon smady would raise a work song. You would hear a man strike up something like,

'Hill an' gully ride-ah!'

And the rest o' workers would chorus, 'Hill an' gully!' It was call and response, and as dem sing, dem dig in time to the song; with the implement hitting the ground in time to the rhythm:

Hill an' gully ride-ah!
(Hill an' gully)
Hill an' gully ride-ah
(Hill an' gully)

> An' yu bend dung low dung!
> (Hill an' gully)
> An' a low dung bessy dung!
> (Hill an' gully)
> Hill an' gully ride-ah!
> (Hill an' gully)

Man, that song would go on and on, with everybody taking turn to
throw in a line to rhyme or which sounded cute. The men were
working hard now, for that bush land was bound to be tough, but the
singing kind of took their minds off the hardness of the labour as they
started to bus' a heavy sweating in the sun hot.

Little after that first song, they now had the appetite for more and
before long another song would start. Meanwhile, the women had fi-
dem work section under full control. Those who a weed grass,
clearing bush or planting would strike up their own songs when the
diggers had a pause:

> Helena an' her mumma go a groun'
> (uu-huh!)
> Helena start bawl fi har belly
> (uu-huh!)
> Go home Helena
> Go home Helena
> Go bwoil *ceresse* fi yu belly
> (uu-huh!)
> The mumma she dig an' she plant
> (uu-huh!)
> but har mine just a run 'pon Helena
> (uu-huh!)
> She pack up her basket an' bag
> (uu-huh!)
> An' go home fi go look 'pon Helena
> (uu-huh!)
> When she reach, she see de bun pan a fire
> (uu-huh!)
> She bawl 'lawd mi one pickney dead'
> (uu-huh!)
> Gal a what dis yu bwoil fi yu belly?
> (uu-huh!)
> from yu baan come a worl' yu no know ceresse
> yu go bwoil *night sage* fi yu belly!

Plenty of those work songs were directly related to true stories. Sometimes, a thing that happened a long time ago, before *Wappy kill Filope*, would get turned into a song and by that it would be a way of blowing warning to others to beware, or else of bringing to memory an incident that happened to people we knew or merely heard about. Sometimes you would even find that people from another parish had a different version of the same song, but there's no surprise in that. Those women doing the cooking never used to sing, for it was wrong to sing over food, or even to prepare food without wearing a tie-head.

Stir it up

Work day is a hungry business, so the food part is very important, and while the digging and the singing was going on, a group of women would be preparing breakfast; cocoa-tea, ackee and saltfish, johnny cakes, bammy, roast breadfruit.

When it was good and ready, the aroma filling up the camp and setting your *mouth-water* running, one of the women would grab the terrangle and beat it or else blow the conch fi mek dem know seh breakfas' ready. You would never see men down tools so fast.

This time, the pickney dem have a pail full up of water to wash the workers' hands. After dem wash-up done, those fellows would just go grab up a mug o' steaming hot cocoa-tea and a bowl full of food.

I would carry over my father's meal to give him, for he was a man who always made sure everybody else get fi-dem first, and if you never mind sharp he would go without. As he took it, he would thank me, saying something playful and then he would 'give thanks' before eating. As him a eat you would just see him taking stock of how the work was going on, his grey old eyes lighting up like a secret joy. And as soon as he finished, he would drink a *yabba* full of water, rinse out his mouth, and he was gone on inspection with a little piece o' cigar in him mouth and his big water boots caked up with clay. This time his face was just gleaming in sweat and contentment.

As soon as breakfast was done, you'd hear, 'Weeeaah!', that was the goat being butchered for the next meal. Maas Noah, the butcher, would just string him up 'pon wan tree a little way off and just cut the throat. After that he would go back to join the work party and the women would take over; skinning the carcass and dressing the meat.

One of the things I also remember about the digging match was helping with the cooking. Work days would come in like a feast day with plenty good food and we would all eat we belly full.

The women would cook a huge *galley* full of goat meat and another *bella* would be used to cook the hard food; yam, banana, breadfruit, co-co, dasheen, badoo, corn, pumpkin and the big cartwheel dumplings, those ones made from young flour that as you bite into it, it cry out, 'whilly'.

If the men were working close to smady yard, then the cooking would happen inna kitchen and we would just carry everything out to the workers. Otherwise, we would catch up a fire near where the work was taking place, collect plenty fire-wood and do all the preparation same place in the open.

The women would be telling stories and catching up with the 'news' about such and such a person, and giving out gossip; who *deh* wid *who-fa* husband, who a breed and who breed dem, and which 'ole hypocrite' was in church but still living 'like Jezebel or King Ahab'.

We children would strain our ears to hear all those kinds of juicy, big-people talk, but we would dare not speak or let anybody notice we were listening. Older people never used to mek fun to let pickney know that we and them were not familiar.

What a commotion the work day when Miss Myrtle Anderson's mouth get 'way wid her and she announced how Miss Violet Hanson and Parson Wedderburn were taking the commandment to 'go forth an' multiply' a little too serious, for fi-dem church meetings after hours had nothing to do wid holy ghost business.

Miss Aggy Franklin started to *trace* Miss Myrtle warning her to watch her mouth and be careful how she speak about Miss Violet, her second-cousin-twice-removed. Miss Aggy told Miss Myrtle, 'is only ignorant people talk what dem no know'.

Miss Myrtle, now, dressed back and said she was sorry but is only share she was sharing what she heard, a no scandalise she did a scandalise Miss Violet's name, after all, she and Miss Vi were church-sisters together. 'And, after all, the Bible say we mus' confess our sins one to another,' Miss Myrtle said. To which Miss Aggy simply kissed her teeth and cut her eye in fine style.

It is only the grace of Gaad why Miss Aggy saw reason that day, for she was known to be very brawlish. But, as soon as Miss Myrtle's back was turned, Miss Aggy let everybody know that she and Miss Violet hated one another and hadn't spoken a civil word in five good years yet she couldn't 'stand by to hear her blood being abused by labba-labba-mouth Myrtle. It wouldn't look good,' she said. Everything quietened down for a time after that, then upon a sudden, hear Miss Aggy, 'Heh-heeeh! so Weddy a ride Hanson ole cow, no? Wha' gwine over-come. Yu do well, bwoy!'

Well, what manner of hilarity erupted over that!

It turned out that Miss Aggy wasn't in the least concerned about Miss Violet's good name, for she same one took over the job of broadcasting the scandal from that day, till people began calling her, Aggy-*Mout-a-Massy*.

As they were talking during this time, some of the women would be beating out coffee or cassava in the mortar, peeling food or attending to the cooking pots a-fire. Meanwhile, a little pickney had the job of fanning the fire and making sure there was enough fire-wood.

As soon as that meal was ready, smady would bawl out, 'food ready', or beat the *terrangle*. You wouldn't have to call twice, but every man would drop his hoe, machete or fork and race over. By this time the sweat was just dropping off their faces or running down their backs, causing those labourers to glisten in the sunlight, like they had been anointed. They would grab a bowl full of *mannish water* or a little *pot-water* before eating anything. That soup would just clear off the gas and awaken the appetite for the main meal. And when you saw that food being shared out and people began to eat; how sweet it was. There is nothing like eating good food when you are well hungry, having earned that appetite.

And while the eating was going on, the talking was just as appetising. Some a chat people business and all a gossip, some a run joke or a tell story while others just a work dem mouth up and down a nyam, for when food is so good, conversation can wait.

Afterwards, joke a give joke, story a give story and who naa talk a listen, and who naa listen a laugh.

As they finished eating the first share, the labourers would go get more till all the food was done, then drink cold water or some coffee. Most would clean dem teeth with a chaw stick or with charcoal, or pick dem teeth with a little tooth-pick. Who smoke pipe, smoked dem pipe or cigar; resting under the shade of a nearby tree; serenaded by humming bees, crickets and doctor-birds; catching a puss nap while the food digested.

Then, while the women cleared away everything and started washing, the men-folk would gradually get up ready to go back to work till evening came and it was time to go home.

> Now the day is over; night is drawing nigh;
> shadows of the evening, creep across the sky.

Maybe tomorrow, if the job wasn't done, they would meet back same place till every inch of ground work was finished. Then, it would be time to move on to the next person's place and do the same all over again.

A hard road to travel

The poor people in this land have known hard work and hard times. When I say poor, most times I mean materially poor, for roots people – natural people; people who are at one with nature – are very rich in spirit.

As children, we would see some groups going out to break rock-stones to earn a living; men, women and young girls. They would sit close together along the road-way, and break those stones with mallets and hammers, sometimes converting rocks into powder; the thankless toil making their hands as coarse as boot-leather. This time the *malata busha* on his horse would drive them on to do their miserable labour in the scorching heat.

Wash day was another type of work day. The women would have their heap of washing doing by the river. Every one of them had on a tie-head and would even wear their clothes in the river; with their sleeves rolled up and skirts tucked into their drawers, scrubbing the stubborn dirty clothes on the rock-stones. What was too dirty or stained, they would carry home to boil.

My best friend Margie told me about one of her aunties who lived a good distance across the island, over in St. Mary. One time she and a whole set of women went to the river for wash-day. They washed everything; laying out their sheets and white garments to bleach in the sun and once the meanness of their chores were done, they even caught some fish and roasted them by the river bank, breaking up the monotony of their labour to enjoy a picnic of roast fish, roast breadfruit with tomatoes and cucumbas that grew wild along the area.

By the time they finished and were ready to leave, it started raining and the river started to swell up; all come in like it would wash them away downstream.

They were rushing to come out, stepping on the flat rocks in the river when all upon a sudden, Margie's auntie stepped on a big flat 'rock' and it started moving. She was too shocked to even holler and by the time she *tek a stock*, it wasn't a rock at all, it was an alligator, and the *sinting* railed up, sending her tumbling into the water. It was getting ready to bite but luckily some fishermen on the river managed to hook the beast while Margie's auntie got away clear.

Could you imagine such a thing ?

Marcus – never live in vain

Marcus Mosiah Garvey I remember. My uncle Nathan and my bredda, who did go a' Panama, were Garveyites and they always used to say things like, 'Stan' up black people, unno no fi bow down, unno fi stan' up straight an' strong. Be a conquerer not a slave.' They had another saying, 'Don't lean on others be a man stand on a footing of your own; be independent if you can and achieve a sound backbone'.

Uncle Nathan always had his old newspapers which he delighted in telling me had been printed by a black man – 'black like we, not brown'. One of them was called, *Our Own* and another one, *The Negro World*; how they were yellow and misabused, that is all I can remember for how Uncle Nathan did handle them often and they were aged, although he tried to keep them well; wrapped up in brown paper. From what I can recall, he always used to dress up most agreeably to go to meetings clear over yonder with his Garveyite *combolo*. One time, when I was young, he carried me with him go clear a' Elderwise Park for a Garveyite convention and Garvey paraded round on a white horse majestically with white feathers in his hat. We stayed up in town for nearly a week with a family called the Bartons. They were very nice people; the father was a teacher and the mother used to teach Sunday school, and for the time we were there, from one hour running into the other, Uncle Nathan and Missa Barton used to chat politics and about world affairs; all some places I never ever heard of before, like Russia, and about things I was sure couldn't have gone the way they said for they sounded so fascinating and awesome. The Bartons had a girl and boy, Joseph and Euphema, who used to carry me and show me around all over. They never behaved like most other town pickney who always came across as spoiled and unmannersable. Some time after that visit Uncle Nathan left country and went to live in town, but he always used to write and encourage me. My bredda and his trade union spars were the same with their beliefs, but to me, they were more flighty and argumentative than my uncle and his friends. Uncle Nathan never used to talk often about his views, so many people had it that it was a lodge he did join, but it wasn't so, not at all. He was a quiet, level-headed man who was never quick to get into an argument about political matters for, before he left to go a town, is bare ignorant people he was living amongst. He encouraged me all the time to 'stan' up 'pon yu own two foot'.

Hear him, 'what man do a' reddy, a nex' man can do. Yu must open yu mind and don't waste time. People who naa go nowhere will always waan' to mek sure yu no go which part yu fi reach in life, so be vigilant me chile.'

I never knew what 'vigilant' did mean and so he explained that it was the same like when the Bible warns us to 'watch and pray'. But, you know, that Garvey was ahead of his time. It's not until years later I fully got to understand what he was trying to progress and how much he was an advocate for we black people in Jamaica. I feel too many of us are blind to see even when we have our eyes wide open; it is as if we are stone blind. Up to today that is a fact. Most of what Garvey preached was a true thing; a good thing, only he never got the *backative*. Listen mek me tell you, you never know what you've got till it's gone.

5
Family Ties

Sow what you reap

When I was about fifteen years old, Old Nat bought a piece of land at Rocky Mountain, a small district way up in the hills of Westmoreland, where the sun kissed the hill-tops and rain and rainbows were very plentiful.

The property, called Five Acres (although oddly enough it measured six-and-three-quarter acres), was a good distance from Hobson's Spring, where we were living at the time. The old man wanted to expand his cultivation area and have an additional place for his family, but not only that. His main objective was to reclaim a piece of land that had been in his family some generations back but which had been lost to outsiders through neglect.

All kinds of cultivation used to go on up there at Five Acres; all over you could see yam hills, sweet potato vines running whe' dem fi run, co-co, banana, dasheen, breadfruit and coconut trees, pimento, pines, ackee, a cocoa walk and a coffee walk. There was even a bit of cane up deh and a small domestic sugar mill, though the main sugar mill was down near fi-we yard.

The mountain property was about five miles from where we lived; uphill walking all the way unless you had a donkey, horse or mule.

Every morning, Old Nat used to get up before day and we had to prepare his quart bottle full of coffee, but we never bothered to put milk with it for he was working around cows and goats so he could just take the milk straight from the animals. He would roast a yam and take that to eat with his coffee, mount his mule and set off for Five Acres. He used to put down my share of the breakfast till when I reached Mountain where, occasionally, I would go and help him work on the land.

After I outed school, whenever I finished all my house duties down a-yard, then I'd go up a Rocky Mountain to do another set of work till evening time.

Now, the way my faada could depend on me made me and him to be very close, coupled with the fact that me was his 'lickle dead-an'-wake baby', had created a strong bond between us.

It wasn't so with my madda, though. I have a feeling she never liked me because I wasn't red-skin like my breddas and sisters dem. Many people don't like to acknowledge that their own parent could possibly dislike dem, but I feel no way; after all, it wasn't my fault Mama acted like she scorned me. Yet for all that, my puppa seemed to compensate by showing me more devotion. As for me, there was nothing I wouldn't do for that old man in return. If his clothes needed washing, I would oblige. When his feet needed washing at night-time, or if him did have *chigga-foot*, dealing with that would be no trouble whatsoever.

Maas Nat was a hard-working man, steady and determined with a strong independent spirit but as he got older, ailments set in and he couldn't carry on running the two properties. Unfortunately, none of the family wanted to help with the management of Five Acres. David, my bredda, said he never wanted to give up his trade as a shoe-maker to take the place over, and my other breddas said they couldn't bother with it either. That grieved the old man after how he had struggled to acquire it and turn it into something viable.

Well, the bwoys left and Maas Nat couldn't manage again, so he decided to sell up. Him did give me one acre for meself and I think it was three pounds an acre him did want for the rest.

In the end, it was a level-headed young man named Peter Bailey, a precocious fellow known all over as Paapa – athough he was young and a single man, he acted very mannish and older than his years – who offered to buy it from him. My faada told Peter to give him whatever he could afford and I think it was twelve pounds that he gave him.

The place at Rocky Mountain had been originally owned by Old Hay, Maas Nat's grandfather. Remember me did tell you how he was born during slavery time? Well, it was him same one who did own Five Acres and so it got passed on to fi-him son, John, but somehow it had been snatched outside the family circle and was very neglected. Maas Nat was determined to re-possess the place and keep it within his family line, so he haggled wid some people calling themselves the owners and paid more for the place than it was worth.

In the end my faada had no choice but to sell up because none a fi-him bwoy pickney dem did waan take it on. But, as fortune would have it, the place still managed to stay in Maas Nat family because as things would later turn out, that is where I was to end up living.

Courting – or as we say – 'talking'

Life funny, yu know. If anybody did tell me that I was going to marry Peter Bailey I would-a tell dem seh dem lie! I used to see him and act like me no see him; keep my head down, and just carry straight on going about my chores. I was never into all that courtship business, no sah. Me was never one of those giddy-headed gals whose tail would ketch a-fire if a man so much as looked at dem. Too much work needed doing for all that. And besides, I figured that if yu was going to honour a man by giving him devotion, he would have to be worthy, and that yu could never know from outward appearance alone; it is no lie that looks is deceiving.

Before him buy off the place at Five Acres, Peter used to work up there as a labourer for my old man and whenever he saw me he would call out, 'mawning' and I would just answer him, 'mawning, sah' and go on about my business. This time me did shy so till! I never used to look a soul in the eye and just that little greeting to a young man used to fill me with nervousness and dread. I just used to keep to meself and mek sure my work was always done when it was supposed to be done. The other pickney dem thought I was foolish for how I was always working like an ole work-horse, but idleness and me were never friends. Truth be known, that was all on account of my strict up-bringing.

In those days pickney couldn't hold big talk with their elders. You had to remember to call men 'maas' and 'sar' – even your own puppa – and to call women 'mam' and 'mistress' and when big people told you to 'jump' you didn't ask how or why – you just made sure you jumped real high.

The thing you have to remember is that men and women were never equals; as a woman or 'girl-chile', a man was always your superior; even your brother could order you about or chastise you, beat you up, too, if that took his fancy. We grew up believing it was the way of

the world. Because I was so hard-working and reliable, Maas Nat
knew he could depend on me, and through how Peter and my old man
were close, I expect he got to see what kind of person I was, until he
must have decided that he wanted to marry me. But, just like before
with my faada, the person Peter's heart was set on first was a woman
named Emily Wanders, from over Bronte way. Only one thing stopped
she and Peter from hitching – that was her tongue. She had it all over
the place that the two of dem did deh, meaning they were already
sweethearts. He never liked that at all so he reacted hard to put an
end to all the rumour and gossip, because he felt she had no right to
carry him business 'gaan abroad', as we say.

He said: 'if she can't keep a secret then she and me caan' inna
nothin' again'.

But the sad thing was that he did really love her and had her up as
a queen. I learned that he was disappointed at how she carried on by
letting her mouth run away wid her and not having any discretion, so
that's what made him put her away.

Anyway, I got to understand that when he left her, she bawl so till!
How she cried; you could tek all the eye-water mek river.

Peter was two years older than me; he was born in 1898. His
father's name was Daniel and his grandfather was called William
Brown. His mother, Sister Eleanora – Sa-Elly – had been Pennycook
before she married Daniel, or Maas Dan as they called him.

Sa-Elly was a registered nurse and used to work down at Harmony
Hall Hospital, down in Rhema. Her mother did name Frances Grant,
from Bullfrog Basin, that is up Rocky Mountain way and they also
had land down at Thatch Valley. I don't remember what Sa-Elly's
faada did name but she had two sisters, Kitty and Elsie. Kitty married
name Black, and she had a daughter named Henrietta while Elsie
married a man named Tate.

After Sa-Elly and Daniel – Maas Dan – were married dem did go
live over Strathbogie before they started to raise a family. Peter was
the last child. His siblings were all boys but for one girl called Lucy.
Later on I think she travelled to Canada and had a family over there.
Peter's breddas were Wilfred who dem nicknamed 'Winkie', he was
the eldest, Aubrey who dem called Jethro, he was a teacher and did
join the Salvation Army, and there was a half-bredda named Joel.

Sammy plant piece a cawn dung a gully

Jealousy and covetousness are very commonplace in this land. It is a seed of destruction in the lives of so many common people.

Around the time my faada bought Five Acres, plenty people used to own land. Even at Hobson's Spring, *nuff* people did have property there because it was so cheap.

They had land for sale at prices so reasonable you would think a give dem did a give it 'way, but despite that, many folks still had their property stolen away by bad-minded and covetous individuals who didn't want to pay even the minimal amount for it. And if they were ever challenged, they would resort to acts of violence. Such people have always existed. They had a way of operating which was to start quarrels by sending their animals over their neighbour's border to eat out their cultivation and create havoc. From the moment the wronged person opened his mouth to say anything, a deh-so war would start. If you no mind sharp, they would tek over your whole place say a fi-dem, and if you objected, they could turn around and kill you. It's not one or two acres my faada lost that way. In the end, he decided that he never wanted all the aggravation, for, as he said, 'when de cruff dead, dem can't tek it wid dem'. So, he left the thieves to keep the land which they stole. As he was getting on in years, it was a relief for him to hand it over to someone as reliable as Peter.

This time you could see why such people used to hanker after our land; from a virtual wilderness, my faada had the place blooming. He planted chinee banana, the small fingered ones, another kind of banana called 'the news' or 'lakatan' some long-fingered bananas, he also planted long dasheen, pumpkin, chow-chow, gungoo peas, patran beans, sugar beans, cucumba – every kind of vegetation. And before bad-minded people tried to do the same for themselves, they would rather take away what we had worked so hard for. There was a song we used to sing that talked about that same thing. It goes:

> Sammy plant piece a cawn dung a gully
> (uh-huh)
> And it bear till it kill poor Sammy
> (uh-huh)
> Sammy dead, Sammy dead, Sammy dead-o!
> (uh-huh)

Sammy dead, Sammy dead, Sammy dead-o!
(uh-huh)
A no thief Sammy thief mek dem kill him
(uh-huh)
A no lie Sammy lie mek dem kill him
(uh-huh)
But a grudgeful neaga grudgeful mek dem kill him
(uh-huh)
Sake-a grudgeful neaga grudgeful mek dem kill him
(uh-huh)

Baby faada

When Peter took over Five Acres from my old man, he never used to trust any and anybody to go up there; he was very discerning, some would say stand-offish. He didn't keep a lot of company.

Anyway, come *pimento* picking time, he used to go to Strathbogie to do his selling, and a young gal named Enid, Edmund Bryan's daughter, used to go up to his yard to help shell the pimento. She was a short *tucko-tucko* gal with not too much common sense.

Peter used to leave out her breakfast and when she finished working, she would cook and cover up his dinner until he came back home.

As it would happen, Enid got pregnant and her puppa asked her who was the father, but she refused to say a word. Everybody now began to speculate that it was Peter's. Down to Peter's own bredda, Winkie, joined in the deliberation that the pickney was his but Peter made everybody know plain seh it wasn't true because him and Enid were 'never inna nothin''. Sometimes, you would stumble across him sitting with his head in his hands and keeping his own counsel while the fuss blew up like a powder-keg.

Through it all, I believed him and felt for him in a way that surprised even me. It was his burden but, for reasons I never quite knew at the time, I felt like it was mine too. All throughout her confinement, Enid kept her mouth firmly shut and refused to say '*kem*' about who did breed her. After the chile was born, Winkie looked 'pon the baby's foot, then he looked 'pon Peter's foot. Hear him in all seriousness, 'I be damn! Pete, own the pickney for him got yu toe.' Anybody with any intelligence would laugh it off, but that cantankerous fool was deadly serious and would do anything to show his bredda off in a bad light. He even went as far as to tell Peter seh him '*corner dark*'. Nobody would believe that that man, Winkie, had travelled go a-foreign; Panama, Puerto Rico, Cuba and such places. For all that, he remained small-minded and, sad to say, ignorant.

Anyway, I got to understand from Peter's neighbour Tommy McGwyer, that Enid's pickney was for one long, *maaga* boy named Kennedy. Tommy told Peter, 'Don't own de pickney because a no fi-yu. Dem trying to *fit yu wid a jacket*.' Tommy told us that it was through his yard the boy, Kennedy, used to walk go look fi Enid when she one was up at Peter's yard shelling pimento in the day time. Kennedy must have offered Enid a hand alright, but it was nothing to do with shelling pimento! But despite the witness account given by Tommy, everybody just came down on Peter to accept paternity and to marry the gal. It was those same people who made Peter stop going a Moravian church, for they carried him to Members' Meeting to get the matter tried.

In those days, the church was the place to get disputes settled, for nobody wanted to go a courthouse. A certain man named Elijah Dennis instigated the action to carry Peter to a Members' Meeting.

On the day that the issue went before the church meeting, Peter went there with Dougie and Tommy McGwyer, the two brother neighbours, as witnesses. They went to testify that it was Kennedy who breed Enid and the pickney a no fi Peter.

In the meeting, everybody sat down patiently, waiting and listening for the matter to be called up. This time Dennis and his combolos were standing very cock-sure ready to play both judge and jury.

After plenty scriptual deliberations, accusations and counter-accusations and bountiful talk of fornication amidst the pimento harvest, Enid finally opened her mouth and confessed that the pickney was Kennedy's.

Me no know if it was the fear of Gaad that got into her when she realised that she was in church and had to swear on the Bible before the Oversight – the church committee – who were going to pass judgement, but she told the truth.

When you looked round, not one of Peter's accusers opened their mouth against him. Elijah Dennis took shame but all the same it fell to him to tell Peter that he was not guilty, which he did most grudgingly. And I don't think they even told him sorry.

After that, Enid had to carry the pickney go a town to register it.

It was Kennedy's pickney and so it was Kennedy dem registered the child, Clarissa Maudlin Kennedy.

That must have been the last meeting Peter attended at that church, for little while after that he decided him *naa* go back deh after how they treated him. Later on he went and joined Church of England. But, even so, after the truth came out, it was as if Peter was still muddied-up with the Enid affair because some people never believed that he was really innocent and some even had it going around that he should have married Enid.

Even years later, on account of that, plenty people never liked me; for they had already made up their minds that it was Enid him should have been with instead of me; while a next set of people had it again that it shouldn't have been me, it should have been Emily Wanders, the woman he abandoned because she was too talkative. Everybody took it upon themselves to map out Peter's life, like him never had a mind of his own.

A no yesterday bad-minded people deh 'bout.

Love letta

Peter was never one of those men who kept a whole heap of company. His friends weren't those galloping wanton types; it was respectable, older people's company he liked to keep; people like Joseph Malpas, Cus Farmer, Baada Justice, Hannah Miller; some of them were older people from my own father's age group, and even he and my old man were friends. Peter and dem would sit down out a hallway or else on the veranda of our house passing the time; a chat go, a chat come.

My bredda, David, and Peter were close pals at this time, and David let Peter know that if a no me him a go marry, him no fi call him friend again. And when Peter decided to write his first letta to me, David was the postmaster! Him bring the missive come deliver it to me, looking over his shoulder first, making sure the coast was clear, then him slide it to me with a 'ssshhh', and motioned that I should put it straight into me apron pocket.

At the first opportunity, me go find somewhere safe to hide it and when I had to go fetch water, I took it out and read it. That was my first ever love letta from a man and for how it set my heart a-thumping, I felt as if it was going to pop out of me ches'.

As a school girl we prepared love weeds for our best friends and for bwoys we secretly admired, but rarely did you tell anybody about it, least of all the bwoy concerned.

Love now, or at least the admission of affection you might feel for a young man, that was a different thing all together. The conveyance of lettas, going and coming, was so secret, it came in like the passing of contraband. True. But courtship had to be secretive, for if the wrong people were ever to find out, they could make your life hell. The first thing you would hear is that you were committing lust or fornication. To certain church-going people, fornication was the deadliest sin, and they used the accusation to try and chastise their fellows all the time. What made it funny was most times those old hypocrites had so many outside children, yet, to them, there was nothing so sweet as putting judgement on others. Those holy-rollers would have found fault with the Lawd himself.

In a small district like ours, courting was everybody's business, so young people used to do their best to keep their affair a secret. Secret? It came in more like sacred. Sometimes, from a young woman had finished reading a letta from her beau or fancy-man, she would all good fi burn it, should in case she was careless enough to put it down where anybody else could clap eye 'pon it. A young woman could be beaten, thrown out of the house or even blackmailed over something so harmless.

Love lettas were like treasure trove. A man might write and tell a woman that he was 'looking at her for such a long time' and how he was 'sure to God him love her world without end'. He might have even called her all kinds of pretty names; 'Sweet-Sop', 'Sugar

Dumpling', 'Honey-Bee or 'Queen Bee', 'Sugar Plum', 'Rose Petal'. All those delightful names would get a gal to be swell-headed, but it would be mistake to let the man know outright that she was in love with him. If she was wise she would tek it steady to determine that it was she alone he was really looking at and that his love was sincere. You had to test the situation, for some men could be very deceptive; filling up many young gals' heads with nonsense and when he got his way, him would a gaan like bad breeze, by which time at least one of them did a-breed. It happened very frequently, and a young gal would lose, not just her innocence, but her character. All too soon, her very youth would be gone. Is the same way it happened to Deacon Tomlingson's daughter, Rachel. She was barely fourteen when a chap from out the area turned her head with talk that he was going to marry her and carry her off go live in his big house in town. Well, nobody no know him people, so all around do dem upmost to shield the gal. They made arrangements to follow him go meet him family, but little more the fellow took off. Not too long after, Rachel too disappeared. Her people found some lettas from the chap, for she and him had been corresponding in secret. It seemed she ran off with the scroundrel. Poor Sister Tomlingson *ban her belly* and she bawl for her pickney gal, but three months didn't pass before Rachel was back and expecting a baby. As for the fellow, she never caught sight of his house in town, only some old boarding house him put her up in clear inna *dungle*, and from he sent her back to her people, he was never seen in our area again.

Dem did have what we use to call shotgun wedding whentime a roguish fellow breed up a gal and never waan' tek the responsibility. But this particular time dem never did find the fellow who defiled Rachel, so the family decided to send her away to live with an auntie in Lucea. When time pickney baan, Rachel came back she one. But from time to time she would steal away to go see her chile, although it never grow with her. In our day any gal who did leave har puppa's yard and run up and down with different men would get called a 'loose gal'. Hell would have to ice over before such a gal could expect to get married, no man would want her. And anyhow a man married a gal only to discover she wasn't a virgin, well, there would be hell to pay for he could put her away and call for all him money and property back. That gal's people now would be in disgrace for how she bring shame upon the family. Equally, if a man did break off his engagement you could sue him for that was breach of contract.

In those days certain men who were very skilful at letta-writing – or who could write at all, for that matter – would hire out dem service to those who wanted to impress a gal. They would produce a love letta packed out with all manner of sweet nothings that would sound scrumptious but it was from a go-between, a hired hand, come to that. Plenty girls didn't care if they ever got to find out, for a love letta was something a gal would always cherish, regardless.

After I did get Peter's first letta, I read it over and over; ran my fingers over the words, held it to my bosom. I even smelled it, and each time I would fold it back crisply and hide it away like a wish. At nights, I could hardly wait to go to sleep and dream about him and the delightful things he had written to me.

This time Ole Jane and my faada wouldn't know anything about it; I couldn't dare tell them I was talking to a man; it could not be done. Even if I was a big, *grey-back* woman in her prime, I still couldn't tell my folks me and a man were moving. Certainly, those things, the mating ritual of letta-writing and conversing, would happen, but in our day they were never talked about.

In that letta Peter wrote, he told me that he really loved me and he took the trouble of letting me know that he had been talking to Emil Wanders but how she let him down. I, now, was his *eye-ball* and he hoped I wouldn't do the same thing. He let me know plain seh if me know me can't keep a secret what happened to the other Emil would happen to me.

Now, not a soul except David knew that me and Peter were attracted or that lettas were passing between us. And in that time, David would do his best to promote the union.

Hear me to him one day, 'David, a love yu love Peter so?' Hear him to me, 'Emil, tek my advice, hold on to Paapa. Whoever else comes along, hold on to Paapa.'

Up to that point, I never used to acknowledge outwardly that I had any feelings for Peter; never used to mek conversation with him or nothing. I wouldn't even call him Peter much less Paapa; it was strictly 'Sar' or 'Mr Bailey'.

One day me and my sister, Florence, were going along and we saw him. He called out a greeting and we answered. He tipped his cap and nodded several times, grinning broadly like we were the good news he had been waiting for all his life. When we passed, Florence said, 'Yu no love him?'

I told her, 'Me no love him at all'.

Hear her, 'Mek we bet him going to be yu husband.'

I said, 'A mussi obeah yu a go wuk.'

She laughed. But, you know, I must confess, the only bwoy I had ever really liked to fondness was called Joe Palmer, who lived just beside us. Me and him used to go a school together; we were practically raised together. Yet he would never know from me that I was secretly in love with him or that I considered him more than as a school-friend and neighbour. But Joe was already engaged to marry a girl from over Redgate, so it was not to be. Still, I used to ask Gaad to give me a husband. In my prayers at night, huddled up in the silence while everybody else slept soundly, I asked the Almighty for someone who would be like a bredda, a husband and a faada to me and the Lawd answered my prayer. It was Gaad who chose Peter for me. I couldn't have chosen a nicer, more decent man. Yes, of course I loved him but before me and him started to move, I always used to tell him to him face seh me no love him. This time David was busying himself trying to get me and Peter together; telling him when I would be going up to Rocky Mountain and where I would be at certain times. That David! Sometimes I would have to pass where Peter was, and when that happened, I would do my best to try and tek time sneak pass so he wouldn't see me, but he would frequently be there looking out for me, all siddung 'pon wall waiting for me, always with a ready smile. Me tell him plain say even if him go a obeah man, me naa go love him. He used to laugh so till. And it was only after we began to correspond that I began to address him as Paapa, and to use other terms of endearment towards him; moreso in the lettas, but never to his face.

Eventually, after lettas passed come and go between the two of us, Peter wrote to Old Nat, my faada. How did that go? Old Nat was a church member at Carmel, so Peter wrote a letta and put it in Miss Dawes hymn book and told her that after church she should give it to Maas Nat. Later on, the service finished and Maas Nat reached home from church. By this time, I had prepared his dinner of fowl with rice and peas, and had it put down by the fire-side a wait till him come.

When he finished eating, he lit up his cigar and took out the letta he got from Miss Dawes, his church sister. That time I was in the next room a patch up his work clothes for him to wear tomorrow, Monday.

After he read the letta, him put it back in the envelope and call me. I went in and he said: 'see wan letta me get'.

He took it out and started reading it. My heart sank, bam! Then he stopped and gave it to me to read. The letta began, 'Dear Brother Natty, I am in love with your daughter Emily …' After I started reading it, I began to cry. The long eye-water just started to run down my face and even started wetting up the letta, so I stopped reading.

Hear Maas Nat, 'What happen, yu can't read it?'

I said, 'No, sah.'

Then him asked me if I loved Peter. Me tell him me no know – after me couldn't *fast* go tell him yes! In those days me would hear, 'so yu a turn woman'.

Anyway, part of me was waiting; expecting Old Nat to say him a go write back and tell Peter, 'no, not my daughter', but instead the ole man told me to 'write and tell Peter that he should come and mek the two of dem sit down and chat 'bout it'.

My heart never beat so hard all the time I was writing the letta, and my hand did shake so much, the writing must have looked like some insect or crab had fallen into the ink-pot and crawled across the paper.

Me seh! The day came a week later, and Peter arrived carrying a bottle of rum. It was a Sunday evening and me did cook and put down him dinner till him come. I was on my way out to fetch water out at Redpan when I met him a go up a fi-we yard, dressed up smart in a suit and tie, looking awkward and more handsome than I had ever beheld him, but nerves overtook me so that I couldn't even bear to look up in him face. He asked me if I wanted him to turn back with me go get the water but I told him, 'no, sah, gwaan whe' yu a go'. He laughed and gave my cheek a playful pinch, his first touch, at which I almost died. All the way to the pond my heart skipped; it danced; it float out me body and go back again; the water pail felt like a hat 'pon me head. I was Sheba, and how I sang; the nightingale never sounded so sweet.

When I came back with the water, Peter and Old Nat were sitting down talking, the rum bottle half empty and the sun preparing to call it a day. Dem chat go, dem chat come. I went into the next room, cleaned out me ears-hole and placed my head up against the wall to hear some of the argument!

'Mek me tell yu Pete', Old Nat said, 'yu really going to have a good wife, for she don't run about and she don't keep no whole heap o' company.'

When I heard that, I knew for certain he'd agreed to the union but my shyness overtook me and I started wishing Old Nat would tell him that me was a thief so he wouldn't want me! Of course, nothing of the sort happened, for Maas Nat gave his blessing.

Anyway, the rum flowed like the rivers of Babylon and the two of them kept up their argument the whole evening. Peter never went home that night; a fi-we yard him sleep right next to Old Nat. From then, Peter and me were engaged to be married.

A little while after the news got round, a man named Lee Pratt said how Peter had ventured to Hobson's Spring come get the best woman and talked how him did have him mind set on me.

Me tell him, 'Yu feava fart, me no want yu!'

This time me couldn't cuss mek Old Nat hear, or there would be trouble.

When Aunt Ione heard I was getting married, she came down, but because I was so shy and with all the excitement, I started crying. Aunt Ione asked me why I was weeping and wondered if I didn't like the man.

I just said, 'Me no know.' I was just a simple country girl, after all, and didn't know how to express my feelings or to bear the burden of being the centre of attention.

She said, 'This is yu first love, don't mek it pass yu by.'

She couldn't have spoken a truer word, but as far as I could see, my whole life was going to change and only Gaad knew if it was going to be for better or worse. Me never know anything about courting or matrimony and there was no bosom friend to tell me what to expect or advise me, so of course I was anxious.

I had heard about certain people who prepared young girls well for marriage. They were mainly old *nanas* who knew what to do to make sure a young girl was properly taught how to be a good wife or, truth be told, concubine. Even through courtship they would tell a gal how she was to behave, the correct way to address a man, carrying herself well, and as soon as the marriage was announced, they would take the girl aside for weeks to make certain she would be properly trained and well fed. What manner of bathing she would undergo, even having her body anointed and prepared for her husband's good pleasure. Those kind of women did come in to me like feather-bed brides. Me no mean they wouldn't have to lift straw, but fi-dem life was more about pleasuring a man than anything else. The nanas would teach the gal how to cook, clean, sew and to watch her mouth so she would respect the husband as her lawd and master. But most of all, she would know how to please him carnally. By the time of the wedding, that gal would know how to behave, whether inna kitchen or in her husband's bed-chamber, but heaven help her when she done breed and her youthful days were over; for most times those men would find another young gal like she was and have her trained up by those same old nanas, and so de circle would run.

Now I did already know how to cook and clean and sew quite well, but as for matters of pleasing my future husband, there was no-one to teach me. Although, come to think of it, me no too certain me would a want to undergo that kind of training to live like servant and harlot for a husband. Me no think that was the kind of woman Peter did a look for anyway. He knew already that I wasn't one of those *sof' soap* gal whose pride was to indulge in dem body. He wanted a woman who would be a help-meet and a good companion, and for that, I had a feeling I was well able.

Old Aunt Ione couldn't tell me what was going to happen on my wedding night or what to expect from marriage, but as it would transpire, that Paapa! Man, me get meself a husband and a half.

6
Market

Oh, Lawd, what a night, not a bite
Not a quatty wo'th sell

Blue drawers, bulla and sprats

After Maas Nat agreed that Peter and me could marry, there was no real commotion around the place, and, for a time, life carried on as normal. It wasn't a quick, hurry-up kind of wedding, and no need for the gossip-mongers dem to speculate about whether or not me was pregnant. The reality was that once we had the blessing from both sets of parents and the banns were posted, things just went back to how they were before, while all the planning was going on, but not in any haste. In fact, we were just two very humble people who never wanted to draw any attention to ourselves, so we kept the news close within family circle. Besides, we still had our everyday lives to lead and work was such a big part of that.

Me always used to go a market, that was one of my main errands. One or two times as a youngster, I had followed Auntie Christie go a Victoria or Jubilee Market in Kingston, and that was quite an experience, but when me come of age it was usually Belmont,

Newmarket and Whitehouse markets we would go.

Most times is before day me set out and quite often it was in the evening, when sun a dip down inna sea before me set off back home. Sometimes, if me was unlucky, is me alone and the *blinkeys* would be travelling home together, how it did late. At other times, me would be on so much haste that me would reach home quick and they would ask me, 'yu get drive?'

I would answer, 'Me sah? No sah! Me lead meggie and drive chenkie' – pointing to my two bare feet.

Those times when I was hurrying, not even my best friends could call me to wait for dem because me was not stopping. Sometimes, on the way to market, we would all run a race to see who would reach the market first. Or, another time, we would drop off one load part way and go back home for another load.

Nowadays if me foot dem refuse to go anywhere, nobody should complain for is plenty walking dem do already in years gaan by.

Market day is a serious business. You would have to prepare everything from the day before and on market day, we would wake up very early, when dew-water was still underfoot and the moon and stars still overhead. That time, everything was so still and the air fresh, crisp and even chilly. Who going a market with you might-a sleep over at your yard. Who naa go, still a help get everything ready. There was always co-operation and it was the women running the show.

So, we would get up soon-soon, wash our face and acquaint our bodies with soap and water, and get ourselves in order. Next, the thing to do was to put something solid in our belly and drink some strong, hot coffee or cocoa-tea, well sweet. Then load up the donkey, if we had one, two big panniers on each side, or else pack our goods up in a basket, make a cotta and carry the basket 'pon we head. At last, we were ready, and pretty soon, we gaan. This time, all around is quiet; everyone, even the lowly animals are still resting. The cock might have crowed for the first, 'Give-me-me-drawers', so you'd better watch out for it was many, many miles we had to travel, on a donkey, if we were lucky, if not, all on foot. Like me seh already, market day is a serious something. On the way we would meet all kinds of people going our way; some on horse-back, others riding mules or donkeys, plenty on foot; all bare foot to that. As we were going along, like purposeful ants, I would over-take some, some would over-take me.

I would call out 'howdy-do' to them all and me gaan. This was no time to stop and pass the time of day.

When I reached the market, there was pure hustling and bustling; so much clutter, people everywhere. I would select a pitch and set me goods out, ready to start marketing. As it got hotter, some would put up umbrellas, or else would be wearing broad straw hats, while some would put up a make-shift shade, maybe using a sheet or coconut thrash. People would come and buy early for that way they would get the best choice of goods. Standards were very high; you couldn't carry any and any *dibby-dibby* or *fenky-fenky* goods to market. If your goods were bruised or rotten, people would cuss you and nobody would buy. They would tell you, 'is hog food yu a sell'. But most people were self-respecting and would always carry the best of dem produce. Most times when I would go to Newmarket or Belmont market to do my selling; a big tray or basket on me head, full of yam, bananas, dasheen, breadfruit, plaintain, pines, sweet potato, ackee, skellion, thyme, everything. Sometimes, you would haggle or maybe trade one set of goods for another. People would always come and buy off my goods soon-soon because my produce was always sound. Those who knew me by reputation would come regularly and if they bought a certain quantity, I might give them one or two extra to reward their loyalty.

When I finished selling, I would go over to the meat traders to buy me pork, beef or seldom mutton. I have always had an appetite for pork, and whenever I had the opportunity, I would buy plenty and *corn* some, and jerk some. The traders dem would say, 'yu like yu pork.' And I would reply, 'yes man, for it is the sweetest meat.'

Certain of my church people were against the eating of pork, but none of dem could ever convince me to give it up. *Fi wha*?

From the meat stall, I would go on to buy the rest of goods to carry home; they would sell flour tuppy-a-quart (we never used bother say 'penny ha'penny'. Most times we used to say 'tuppy ha'penny' or just 'tuppy'), then maybe some spice, salt, matches and some coconut oil.

Certain times when me reach in from market, me would cook callaloo with pork fat. Often, the others would have cooked already, but maybe callaloo is what I had a hankering for, so that is what I would have. We used to grow callaloo a-yard in the garden beside the house, but sometimes you could pick it a roadside because some people working out a road would either drop callaloo or else planted it as they were going along and it would just grow and whoever wanted it would just help themself. Me used to collect some big bundles along my journey from market, help myself to the vegetables growing freely along the wayside, and even give some away. And when me cook it up with fish or pork fat, it did nice so till!

I even used to buy sprats from Whitehouse where we would go there to buy fish. Whenever me did go, the fishermen would full up me pudding pan with sprats and if I never have enough money, they would trust me until the next Wednesday. I was such a good customer, they never had to ask me for their money. They used to tell me that if everybody was like me, there would be no trouble in the world. After buying everything I wanted, I would hurry on home to roast those sprats. When the sprats finished roasting, me used to sell them by the dozen and give half dozen extra to my loyal customers. That way, they would always buy from me. I would always make a profit since me used to buy the fresh fish cheap-cheap; a whole heap for just tuppy and I would sell the roasted ones for truppence a dozen.

You know what was nice? Roast sprat and bulla cake. If you had a fancy, you could even add a peg or two of puss prayers – avocado – and that would be quite a little feast. Sometimes the Belmont traders would come up to Rocky Mountain to sell dem goods; crisp fried sprats, pepper shrimps, lobster, 'Miss Pretty'. 'Parrot' and other types of fish we called 'ghutto'. They also had *blue-drawers*, bread, cakes, pone, all kinds of good things, so it was a delight whenever they ventured up our way.

One time, a man who live close to us got instructions from a local physician called Dr. Johnson that he wasn't to eat any kind of fish whatsoever, and he wasn't to eat ground food either. However, this particular occasion when the Belmont traders came up with dem delicacies the certain man mek him wife go buy sprats and told her to cook a piece o' yam to eat with it. As soon as he finished eating, the man dropped down dead – dead till him teeth 'kin. News-bearer met Dr. Johnson with the tragedy. You see what *hard ears* can do? He knew he wasn't to eat that kind of food, but I suppose who can't hear will feel. I was just glad a no fi-me sprats him did eat mek people go say a me poison him!

Lef' foot boot

As I am talking about markets, me mind run on a certain incident that happened one time at Newmarket.

A fool-fool gal named Monica run in the place like she was demented and come tief two lef' foot boot. It must have been a pair of boots she did aim to tek, but is two odd foot she get away with. She only managed to grab them and run quick go hide inside Maas Ben's tinsmith shop, and as she rushed in, she flung the boots over the counter. But some people from the market run down Monica and ketch her. They carried her up a police station and charged her fi larceny. As you can imagine, everybody have the gal up as a laughing stock after that; for how she could go clear a market, inna broad daylight go tief two lef' foot boot! Most people did know already that she was kind of simple, but dem never realised seh Monica did so fool! But all the same, she was lucky, for most people who stole from a market would get such a beating, (that is if dem never lose dem life). Most times too, the police might have added beating to beating when they carried a thief to the lock up. It wasn't unusual in any market place or community for a tief to get stoned to death or even to get his hand chopped off with a machete. A no lie. If a man steals through hunger, then that is something most reasonable people can understand but, mark you, some people would just act first and ask questions later, so they wouldn't even bother to find out if it was hunger that drove a man to be a thief. Stealing was something that most people would get ignorant about.

As far as market people were concerned, dem put down dem property and nobody no business fi go trouble it.

Busta

I well remember the Wednesday when Bustamante came to Belmont market; what a commotion!

That day I did go a' Belmont the same as always with my produce to sell, and as it would happen, that was the day they brought Bustamante to show him around. As usual, we went in the market quite early and set out our goods ready for the day's trading, then, suddenly, smady cried out,

'Come now, come see *Busta*!'

'Whooa!', everybody cried out, then all you could hear was bare noise and, when you looked, a big crowd was pushing in the direction that Busta was coming in. People all leave dem trade and run gaan look. Dem no business 'bout thief, dem no business 'bout dem customer.

Man, they say Jamaica people wild, but what a thing that day; me never see such excitement 'from me baan come a worl''. People were pushing and shoving, cussing and clawing their way through to look 'pon a mortal man just like them-self. In all the melee I did manage to glimpse Busta but I was never in all that carry-on, after me never able go get lick-dung and trampled under foot just for trying to look 'pon Bustamante's face. Him a did who? By that, I don't mean to say he wasn't somebody important, I know he was a very special man for we Jamaicans, especially for black and poor people, but the way they did carry on that day you would think it was Gaad Almighty himself coming in a' Belmont market! But when you saw Busta back off him shirt now and started to say 'Jamaica people should be set free' – man, it was that time people got excited. It came in like he was ready to show how he was prepared to fight for the common people and that won him no little fame and adulation. In those days, black people were always lower down the scale of life; they never directly had slavery as before, but it wasn't too far off. When Busta talked about independence and about making things better for the blacks, it come in like he was Moses who did come to lead the people to the Promised Land. People did really feel it, you know. Hear the whole heap of jackasses crowding round, 'Wheeaaa!', and then they started pushing and shoving all the more. I tell you, I was just content to look at a picture of Busta and be satisfied; I couldn't carry on like I was mad over a politician. If me did carry on so, how me would-a gwaan in the Second Coming when Jesus Christ comes back? Me seh, mah! I never saw such a thing inna Belmont before or since as the rally with Busta that day. After he looked around Belmont and gave his speech, they carried Busta down to Sav-la-Mar to do the same and some people even followed on from the market, the excitement spreading like when dry bush-land ketch a-fire.

7
Married Life

Wedding day

When the time came for me and Peter to get married, I was so nervous; the whole of the Friday night before the wedding, I never slept a wink. I just bawled the whole night long; it must have been just before day-break that me ketch a little nap. Why was I bawling? Because I was anxious and never knew what I was getting into. Me and Peter had never spent time stepping out together in a courtship way; finding out about one another; I never knew if he was going to be a good husband or if I would be a good wife. I just never felt prepared, and, for how me did a fret, it was nobody's business. As a man, I knew he was decent enough and hard-working, but, aside from letters and the barest of chats, (nothing intimate for we never did deh, so to speak), we had never shared with one another our dreams and hopes for the future, so I wasn't to know what married life with him would be all about. Those things were strange to me, and on top of that, I never had any close bosom friend to counsel me. But, now the time had come. That must have been the longest Friday night of my life, yet come the morning, not a soul was to know that anything had been troubling me.

Peter's best woman was called Maud Campbell and my best man was Joe Palmer, (my former school mate, neighbour and church bredda). Joe's sister, Jess, came over early to help me dress and get ready. My maid of honour was Sa-Elly, Peter's mother, who we called my 'blessed madda-in-law' and Margie, my best friend, was my chief bridesmaid. I was Church of England and so by now was Peter, but we got married in the Moravian church as it was his people's place of worship. In the morning when I awoke, I could barely eat a morsel of my breakfast, mackerel and banana, all down to nerves, but they made sure I had something hot to drink.

My wedding dress was white and very delicate. It was a lady named Miss Maud from Kilmarnoch who made it. I don't clearly remember the style, but it did look like something out of a picture book, and I had white gloves and white shoes to match. I had a godfather named Tailor Powell, who was a tailor by trade, and his wife, my godmother, called Cassie, both lived over at Carmel and between them, they made plenty of the clothes which the wedding guests wore that day.

I always used to wear my hair in two or three big plaits, for it was always very thick and long and it seems me did get some of the coolie hair from my grandmother. I never used to fuss with it, I just kept it very plain and simple. You know, old time people used to say, 'yu hair is yu beauty', and they would encourage us always to take care of our hair, even to the point of treating it like something sacred. Me did never get blessed with pretty looks, so it come in like the good hair me get was my one point of beauty fi true, although, to my heart I still believe that beauty is as beauty does; pretty looks have nothing to do with it. As far as the hair went, me never used to do anything more than groom it with castor oil and plait it or, whenever I washed it, I used to put it in *chinee bumps*.

I don't rightly remember how me did wear it for the wedding or, for that matter, anything about the head-dress, but Jess and the other women helped me fix it up. It might even have been the first time in my life I had ever worn it out loose, in all its glory, I can't recall. To finish off, Jess put a little Kuss-Kuss perfume 'pon me neck and a little 'pon me wrist. Throughout it all I was so sober that they had to remind me that is a wedding not a funeral I was going to, and my wedding come to that.

Dressed now, and feeling like a princess from story picture book,

I could hear a noise outside the house. It was still very early in the day and, as usual, the market traders were going about dem business, or who a go a Sabbath service were preparing themselves, otherwise people were just going about their domestic affairs. The noise I had heard, of horses cantering, was Peter come to collect me with his two beasts; one horse fi-me, one fi-him. We never rented a car like some people who made a big show and hired vehicle for fi-dem wedding-day. Way out in the country which part we were, there weren't any good roads for the cars to drive on; they had to park up and the people would get out and walk for all that pomp and parading. Yet still, for such an occasion, all who were poor like church mouse, would turn poor-show-great for wedding day and hire cars, which was rare enough sight and an expensive luxury those times even for folks in town.

To tell the truth, it was mostly family and close friends who attended fi-we ceremony. The wedding wasn't an open invitation to people from all over yonder, and, on account of that, some got vexed. In those days, people used to try and hold competition to have fi-dem wedding bigger than the next person's. When you go fi see people! That was how certain individuals had it that they are really smady in the area, through dem hold big wedding and have car a lean 'pon its side. You know, a wedding day affair could be such a spectacle, like the occasion when Eleanora Robertson get spliced with Percival Matterson; my oh, my! It feava the whole o' Jamaica was in attendance; all now people still a come from all over, (and the debts dem still a pay fa!) Eleanora and Percival had ten ten-pound cakes, each of many layers, the bride had ten bridesmaids, ten maids of honour and the groom, ten best man; ten of everything. And everybody was dressed, you know, to the hilt, and even the cakes were trimmed with some of the bridal veil. The cake-bearers put the cakes 'pon dem head and danced skillfully through the gate and up to the church-hall which was hired for the reception, and as they danced and twirled with the cake still a-top dem head, the people sang, 'welcome, welcome', and waved a white 'kerchief. It was a sight to behold.

Some people, our very neighbours, held it against us that we never had such a show wedding, and some of dem even went as far as to say we never truly married, because dem never see transportation packed up with people straining to climb the hill and struggling to negotiate a pass through those terrible backwoods countryroads. We never turned ourselves into any kind of *pappyshow*; we were just humble people, who were never into all that carry on and just had a simple, quiet wedding without a whole heap of people, parade or fuss. The wedding was a small affair; nothin' fancy. My faada, Old Nat, couldn't go because him did sick but before I left the yard that morning, he started bawling like a baby. He must have been crying because, since me was getting married, he felt he was losing his eyes, his right hand, his feet; everything, for remember, there was nobody else he could rely on like me. It was, to all intents and purposes, a turning point, for I was no longer in their eyes a mere pickney gal; I was becoming my own woman.

All the same, nerves got the better of me that Saturday; I was shaking like a new-born puss. Although I can't remember all what and what took place, it is still one day of my life I shall never forget. Peter wore a white jacket and a pair of coloured pants, shirt and tie, with a pair o' shoes shine till you could see your face in dem; you didn't need a looking glass.

His hair was cut, but it wasn't too low, with a sharp parting down one side and him did have a clean razor shave and I can't be too certain what again for how little I managed to look at him, in him face. He was very smart, like English gentleman. In one hand I think he had his umbrella or maybe it was it a fine hat, me no 'member, and in the other hand his big King James Bible, shiny as his shoes. Most of the time my head was bowed down like I was inspecting the floor and no amount of pleading would persuade me to raise it up for any length of time; two minutes and I was back on floor inspection while my heart raced like unfettered young mules. I only remember the part of the service when the parson announced that Peter and me were man and wife together, and everybody clapped and hooped. As to the rest, it did just *swips* by so fast.

After the church, there was a little celebration feast down a-yard. Aunt Ione had made a big cake and there was plenty of food, curry goat and such like, but, no my dear, we never had a big, costly *gerrey*. I was lady-queen for that one day but if only I wasn't so shy and nervous, maybe I would have enjoyed it better. Call me foolish, or you could even say I was naive, me no mind. But I wasn't brought up to be bold or self-confident, otherwise they would have said I was *facety* and the older people would have surely boxed that strong nature

out of me. As a girl chile, you couldn't tek fast set up yourself as
equals with your elders or with any man, for that matter. You had to
be compliant and even meek, right down to women who found
themselves with a fool-fool husband who never knew 'A from Bullfoot' was supposed to look upon that man as her lawd and master.
Any woman or gal pickney who didn't want to know her place would
find a whole heap of opposition to try and break her spirit. But mind
you, is plenty woman me know who did wear the pants in their
domestic circle. They might have been meek from morning but from
they got the wedding ring it was a different story; they ran tings in the
house and the man just had to *satta*. Some women even used to have
their husband around the place like *maama man*; a cook and clean
and wash clothes while she took on the serious responsibilities like
money affairs. I saw it already growing up. It never go so with me and
Peter, though. We went on as loving as ever – although if certain
wicked people had dem way we would have mashed up and a-fight
like *hag and daag* from the hour we stepped over the threshold, but
I'm coming to that.

Wedding ring

When I got married, little did I know that the wedding ring which
Peter put 'pon me finger would land me in court.

One night, coming up to Christmas, I dreamed about a local woman
I knew named Lydia. She was a dressmaker in the district, who was
responsible for training plenty young people in that same trade.

Lydia was one big, red, *bully-riging* kind of woman, who loved to
control everything and everyone around her. She liked nothing better
than to dominate every situation and plenty people were afraid of
her. There was no business going on in the district, nothing
happening behind closed doors, that she never knew about. Even if a
certain matter never go so, she would have it spreading as gospel. She
did have a Cuban husband, Columbie, but she had him around the
place like him was a puppy; he couldn't manage her. Hear the
husband to me one time, 'Ma Mel, how it is dat everything dem ask
yu, yu answer dat yu don't know, but whenever dem ask yu sister, she
always know?'

Me say, 'I don't know, sah.'

He took it for joke and laughed but I was serious because I never wanted anybody minding my business none-at-all, especially those wretches.

Now, this particular night that I dreamed Lydia, in the dream I was going a market and happened to pass which part Lydia and her companions were sitting down under house chatting and minding people's business. As me pass, me call out 'howdy' to dem. At this time now, I wasn't too long married, but troublesome talk had it going round that we were not really spliced. So now, if we no married, a-fornicate we up a yard a-fornicate. To some people, there is no victual as sweet as gossip. I never wanted to boast on anybody that I was a married woman, so I took off my wedding ring and put it inside me pocket so those women wouldn't see it and tease me. A so me dream, plain as day. But as me tek off the ring, Lydia grabbed on to me apron and the ring flew out and got lost. In the dream me see when the ring fly out me pocket; it did just a *kick puppa-lick* till it rolled away under the house where the women were. Little more, in the same dream, me see when they took the ring to a certain fellow, Cudjoe, one *finny-finny* man, for him to work obeah 'pon the ring. Afterwards, dem come give it back to me saying that they had found it. From the moment I took it and put it back on me finger, the up-shot would be that me and Peter would end up fighting like hag an' daag, till we mash up. A so the dream went.

When I woke up, I wondered what it could mean; it worried me so much so I told Peter about it.

He told me, 'Watch the dream, for it has a meaning.'

A couple days later, I set off from up my yard to go to Whitehouse market. Now, as I approached Lydia's yard, I took off me ring, just like in the dream, and put in me apron pocket. Again, just like in the dream, I saw the group of women sitting down under the house, chatting. They were making much of a li' pickney-gal named Lois. The child's madda, Louise, was with them, alongside Lydia and a couple others.

Anyway, that morning, as I saw the women, I made a point of calling out a greeting, and especially to Lydia, before I went over to make much of the little baby Lois, for I always loved children. I said, 'Mawning, Lyddie', (for a so everybody did call her). I knew that anyhow me did pass and never singled her out for special attention, she would have had me up.

She said, 'Who dat know me so well?'

Louise said, 'A Ma Mel', (a so dem did call me).

Hear Lydia, 'Thank you Mistress Bailey, same you see me coming you run.'

I never knew what she did mean, but from I heard her talking in that style, and calling me 'mistress', I knew something was not right. It come in like she had her bait ready for me, and she and her friends were all wrapped up together like a band of thieves; skinning dem teeth and showing me plastic smiles, but what was really going on? Since I married, they would have all wanted me sit down with them and show off me ring and chat with dem about my personal business, but I was never into all that. Still, in the back of my mind I was sure they would bother me about my wedding ring, so that is why I took it off and *shub* it inna me pocket.

As I approached dem, Lydia came up to me. She said, 'Where yu ring? Yu right fi hide it from me. What yu and Peter up deh a do mek yu won't let dat man sleep a' night-time?'

I stood up straight and looked in her y'eye and told her, 'What yu business wid me ring? It pay fa, yu know, and as to Peter, him is me lawful husban'.'

She was clearly taken aback by my boldness, but she never wanted to lose face, so hear her, with her renk self, 'Then because me no have husban' ...'

As she said that, she just grabbed on to me apron and, unbeknown to me, the ring flew out. I told them 'good mawning' and set off about me business, leaving dem chatting and carrying on. I had to reach market and by now it was getting late. A little way from where I left the women, my mind said, 'Emel, where yu ring?' Me reach in the apron pocket, but it never deh-deh. Lawd! What was I to do? I searched all over; no ring. I ran back quickly to which part the women were. They asked me what was wrong and I told dem that me ring was missing.

Hear Lydia, 'A good, for if yu did keep it on 'pon yu finger, it couldn't laas.'

That facety woman even went as far as to say that is duppy tief it 'way from under the house. Bewildered now, I couldn't stand up there and chat with dem, so I ran off quick to reach the market. They called after me to say they would look for the ring till dem find it, but

I never trusted dem.

When I reached down at my faada's place, teary-eyed I told Maas Nat the story and he decided to send some young bwoys up with me to look for the ring, but we never found it. By this, I was certain everything I saw in the dream was coming to pass. I felt sure those women had me ring and were carrying out their evil plan. It was clear by this that the ring had flown out of my apron when Lydia had grabbed on to me.

We went and reported the matter to the church authorities: the oversight, and told dem how that woman Lydia had interfered with my apron and mek me lose me ring. Now, the church would decide on any kind of dispute, and if they couldn't get a verdict, then it would often go to court – up the '*four an' twenty step*', as we called the courthouse. Nobody at all liked the idea of going to court back in those day. Church was the first resort in most cases, and we went with the earnest hope it would be settled there. Now, the ring did cost twelve shillings. It was, apart from my husband and my faada, the most precious thing I possessed, and losing it was like a blow to my heart. So now, we wanted the church to decide the case and to mek Lydia replace the ring that she caused me to lose. When we went for the hearing at Members' Meeting, Lydia told the preacher that she did trouble the apron and might have caused the ring to drop out, but hear her,

'Me could-a dead and go a hell, me naa pay a farthing fi it.'

The preacher told her no fi seh so, and warned her that she was blaspheming in the church, but she was determined. When we saw she was going to be too stubborn, the preacher advised us to carry the matter to court. So, we went to get a lawyer man and Lydia did the same. On the day, as her people were coming into the court, they took time come up to me, draw me to one side and asked me if me really believed me could win Lydia a court. Everybody was afraid of her, yu know, and from what they were saying, it feava me never had any business to challenge her.

Hear one of dem, Dulcie: 'Me could-a married and have on twenty five rings pon me finger an' if Miss Lyd waan' tek dem 'way or cause me fi laas none, a don'na charge her fi it.'

She made it look like a wicked me did wicked for carrying Lydia to court, yet even Lydia's own son, Baldrick, did agree with me because, he said, she shouldn't have done what she did. But another one of Lydia's friends said if she did know we were going to court, she would have gone to see the obeah-man, Cudjoe. I never paid her any mind.

During the trial, Lydia got up, dismissed her lawyer, and let it be known she would defend herself. She acknowledged all that she had done, but she told the court the same thing she had told the church council, that she naa pay for it. The judge threatened her with prison for contempt of court so she agreed to buy a new ring, but we never wanted her to so much as touch a ring and give me, for anyhow she had brought a ring come give me, that would be trouble, so we went back to the goldsmith and ordered a new ring to be made. Lydia's son, Baldrick, paid the twelve shillings cost, not she, but how she despised the young man for that gesture, it is a sin. All the same, we were glad to win the case in court. Imagine saying you would rather go a hell than pay for what damage you caused a person. A no wickedness that?

A no today me under it with wicked people, me own neaga people to that.

Many years later, when Lydia died, her son went to live in her house with his family. One day, one of his children, little Baldrick, was playing 'hide an' seek' with his playmates. The youngster crawled go hide under the bed and from that moment he couldn't talk; him just turned fool. His puppa and the others had it that the pickney had seen his granny Lydia's duppy under the bed, and a that turned him dumb. From beyond the grave she was still causing malice and mayhem.

Me did dream her too one night after she passed over. In the dream, me see Lydia just walking along the road, then, all upon a sudden she turned into a gourd and started rolling, faster and faster like a gig. Me no know what that meant, but me was not afraid, neither did I take it to heart any-at-all.

House and lan'

Married life was quite something. You know, back in the olden days, from a woman got married, it came in like she really achieved something in life. No matter how poor she was or what kind of burden she had to bear; especially if her man was a rum-drinker or was the kind of man who did keep different women along with her, from she got a ring on her finger and could call herself 'mistress', it came in like she gained respectability. She would get her house an' lan', and her pickney dem would get to carry dem puppa name. Most times, if dem no married, is hell some women would go through to make a man acknowledge the children he had with her. Nuff women did have pickney out of wedlock and no tek it fi nothing, and plenty-plenty men and women lived together inna house as common-law wife and husban'. But, you know, for all that, marriage was a sacred thing. It was the kind of institution that some were rushing to get into – especially women, and those who were in it already – especially men – were rushing to come out of. Life!

Love ile

> 'Shine eye gal is a trouble to a man
> she want dis, she want dat,
> she want everything.'

Certain women would be so *red-eye*; everything dem see, dem want. All a man would hear from them is, 'bring it cum gi' me', and they would never be satisfied.

Another type of woman again used to try and 'tie' a man to make him stay with her. See, a woman might go to a obeah-man and ask for 'love ile' to put 'pon the man or else to put in his food, so that no matter what befall, him naa go lef' her. The obeah-man or woman would gladly tek her money and give her something, and she would go carry out all the instructions. If only some of those fool-fool women did use common sense they would realise that the man they were rushing to keep oftentimes would turn out to be the living devil! A so it happened with Maudie Mitchell. That gal go a obeah-man go ask for 'ile-of-love-me-long' to put 'pon Hubert Walker. After that, he would a never leave her; even after him eat out all her money, chased off her mumma out the house and beat the pickney dem till dem run 'way. She could-a beg, she could-a plead, Hubert 'tan same place, walking up and dung telling people how much him love Maudie, and how him vow to love her forever. Imagine, paying money to mek a man 'tan wid yu, or else using black art to take away another woman's man!

Oftentimes, a woman would see a man she loved because he had good looks, a handsome face. What is underneath the surface, she has no idea. What if that man was the kind of person who would beat you and use your supportance go give a next woman? Many people consult obeah man to get a life partner, only to turn round regret it later on when *dem atta claps clock strike*. When a woman and man 'talking' him might come in like Gabriel own self; kind, respectable, the kind of sweet-heart that any woman might want to cut out her heart and entrust it to him. But she might want to marry that fellow, set up house with him and bear him children. If that same man turn round and no waan' marry her, what she a go run him down for? It would come in like he must have a wife already, no true? Or else him mussi waan' spoil her up and put her in a whore-house. Anyhow that woman go have pickney with him, watch and see, for it is then she would a find it hard to marry. It is better to know a man's intention from the first and no try push him which part him no waan' go. Man and beast can be stubborn alike; sometimes out of them and mules me no know which one worse! Affairs of the heart is one place you will always find the involvement of the obeah-man. Faint-hearted people would run go a obeah-man and tell him, 'I'm looking for a good man' or 'I want to hold this woman.' *Lawd-a-massy*! Sometimes it would be better for dem to go straight a hell go invite the devil to come live with dem. Plenty people lived to regret the part obeah played in their domestic life, for how the relationship would go along as good as ever, then, all of a sudden, it would just turn sour. From that happened, there would be no peace in their life, no peace whatsoever.

They had a little song for fun,

> Hilda making wedding plan
> carry me name go to obeah man
> all yu do, yu can't get through
> I ain't going to be married to yu!

And you know, plenty people were truly corrupt. They would see you and your husband or wife living as good as ever and they would do their utmost to mash up your life. A no lie. All that me pass through. All the same, me never stopped thanking Gaad that I got a good husband and there was no sorrow with it and no obeah-man's oil to tie a soul with, for true love will do its own binding.

Heavy-handed husband

I always respected my husband as the head of house, for that was what I went to church and vowed to do, but some of those men in our district never deserved an ounce of respect whatsoever. And you know, vow or not, if my Peter was such a man, I would a never give him the time of day. Respect deserves respect. Heavy-handed husbands were as common as green lizards in our area. Chief of all, there was a certain man in the area called Gideon. He loved a woman named Dorcas, but after she married smady else, Gideon decided to take Hortense for his wife. How that man used to beat his wife, all beat her for Dorcas who he wanted to marry. He beat her because she wasn't Dorcas, he beat her for his sport. Poor Hortense just use to wait till he left the yard so she could hide the piece of board or the *supplejack* he used to beat her with. That wicked man even put nails in the board he used to chastise his wife. Hortense bring it come show me one day. Good God! It gave me great pleasure to set it a-fire, but she knew he had plenty more. People like me used to encourage her to leave him, and she did a couple times, going back to her madda's yard, but her family made her go right back to him. But I couldn't rest over the matter, it was burning me up inside. One day I meet Gideon a come from town, so I called out to him, told him me waan' talk to him. Me tell him seh me was aware how down to the parson see an' blind, and how the rest o' people in the area hear an' deaf, but I knew full well how he was ill-treating his wife. You know, that man denied everything; he was even ready to bawl eye-water seh a lie me a tell. Him love Hortense, him say, to him heart and soul, and how such false rumours got spread about he couldn't tell. How lightning never strike him dead on the spot, me don't know.

Me tell him, alright, but no mek me hear any fresh rumours about any abuse. He couldn't look into my eyes all the time he was talking to me, but me mek him know plain seh Hortense was my church sister so her well-being was my business. It took every ounce of courage to confront him like that, because he was a strong, firm man, but from me know him was in the wrong, me wasn't frightened. Gaad knows, if it did come to it, I would have put up a fight because no man no business fi a lick daag with a board let alone him own wife. The very place where they lived belonged to Hortense before they were married, but it come in like is run him did waan' run her off from there. Gideon was craven for property; anywhere land was selling, he would find himself there buying up, never satisfied. But people knew about his cruelty, even though him put on the show of being a God-fearing man. Hortense underwent years of abuse. It wasn't only the beatings but the way he would take up with different women and she couldn't make a sound in complaint. To make things worse, poor Hortense did have a lame foot and that caused her to walk funny, so people latched on the nickname, '*Hip an' Drap*' but they pitied her nonetheless for her ordeal. Gideon even tried to order who and who she was to call friends and on top of that, he used to try keep members of her family from going to look for her.

Sad to say, that man carried on ill-treating his wife until him beat her kill her. Not a law-man stepped in to prosecute the wretch, and so Gideon got away with murder. You know, from the day of the funeral, that man made certain he never bucked me up square; anywhere him see me, him mek diversion or just turned around and walked away. Poor Gideon, him dead and stink more than Hortense who we buried, but he was the last one to know.

Buried crossway

A next wild man in the area was Clifford Whitelaw. Fi-him wife, Grace, used to get the juice! She did have long, pretty hair and him did have a way to grab it and wheel her around, dropping her on the ground, Baps! Mashing her body on the rock-stones. He used to have him floozy women dem and a whole heap of bastard pickney about the place.

Clifford did have one special woman named Dinah who was everything Grace wasn't – young and carefree. This time poor Grace did come in like nervous wreck. She was just so jumpy all the time, with not an ounce of self-assurance. In those days, yu couldn't tell a woman to leave a man like that, for chances would be he might have run her down and killed her if he got enough encouragement from his rum-drinking spars.

One time a pickney go tell Grace seh him see Clifford a sex Dinah over wall and all what dem a do. Grace mussi tek time go look and Clifford ketch her a-peek. He went after her to beat her like him did waan' kill her. He dragged that woman go clear over tank to drown her. It was one of her sons who came by just in time to rescue her.

Wicked! And he didn't care who knew, for not a soul could tell him no fi do it. Jezan-king-of-mercy! Those men. Women did come in like donkeys to dem how they loved to beat-beat. But even donkeys have their day when beating naa go have any use, or when they will take revenge. Is Grace same one buried Clifford when him dead. A mussi him wickedness mek him go dead before time. At the funeral, they buried him crossway. The right way to bury someone is with their head facing the rising sun, that is East, and with their feet facing West. But Clifford's burial went crossway, that is with his head to the West, and his feet to the East, head down, on account of his cruel legacy; he had behaved like Satan, so they sent him to hell. Everybody decided he never deserved any other kind of send off, and they directed the brute to hell quicker when they buried him crossway.

Miss Contention

One woman we called Miss Contention was a first class bitch. She did have a good husband named Ustas. A sweeter, humbler man you couldn't find, but yet that woman had him around the place like a puppy daag. She never even used to cook and feed him; it was me and another church sister, Evadne, who took pity on him mek him get to eat. Miss Contention hated us because of that, but we never cared. For spite, she'd even send her cow over the border into my field to eat out our banana, corn and such like. When you called and told her which part the cow deh, she would bawl out: 'soon come', but dat-deh 'soon come' could never reach, for she naa mek-haste.

One time in particular, she allowed the cow to come do his damage as usual, and the beast was making ready to go in the boiling house, where we made sugar. While Peter was one of dem *sof' soap*, who never wanted any trouble over it, me mek dem know plain seh me naa stand for it. So I grabbed that chain and led the cow go round to the district pound. In those days yu had to pay money to have the animal released. To the very extreme, some people would take matters into their own hands and kill an animal that strayed over their territory, but according to the law, they had to return the body to the rightful owner. I wouldn't go so far; the pound was enough. Miss Contention did have a DC friend we called 'Pilate' on account of how wicked he was, and it was he who went and paid the animal's poundage on her behalf. That must have made her hate me all the more; me never care. But as to her husband, a nicer man you couldn't find. He was never involved in all that discord. It come in funny though, for I used to cook for Ustas and in all that I never yet left out Miss Contention, for if she asked for food, I would always give her. Plenty-plenty times she would stand up outside my kitchen and eat dinner from me. How could that be, you ask? It was the same Peter mek it go so. He told me plain: 'Gaad seh yu should feed your enemy.'

When him talk so, we never knew that same enemy would turn around and kill him, but I will come to that.

Encouraged by her madda, one of Ustas's pickney gal did fight her father. She took his finger and bite it till it bus', gushing out blood. It was a long time before it healed over, but he couldn't even complain. Another time, Ustas took sick, so me mek soup carry go give him. He said, 'Tenk yu mi aunt, Gaad bless yu, mah'. But he was sick for a long time, and one night I dreamt that I saw a whole heap of people from the district going up to his yard to look for him. In the dream, I also went to visit him, and when I went inside the room he said, 'Lawd, dem a kill Ustas before time.'

I was the only one he talked to in the dream. After he said that, he just died same time. I stretched him out, tied his two big toes together, ban up his jaw and put two pieces of lime over his eyes to keep them shut. The next day when I went up to see Ustas for real, he was truly on-dying. He gave me a blessing before he passed over. I feel certain that if they never ill-treated him, that man would have lived longer. Imagine, plenty women in this world a-look good husband – wanti wanti caan' getti – and yet getti getti no wanti. What a thing!

8
Days of Grace

Buddy charmer

Not too long after we were married, I came to the conclusion that heaven's windows had opened and Grace had smiled especially on me. Peter was my beloved Paapa – for so I now called him after we were married; though that is not all; for he was me buddy-charmer, me love-bug, me pupus, me egg-eye; everything – a joy in my life.

To the sweets of it, marriage is truly a blessing; all too often in those first months, I was Sheba, and the half has never been told. But, complementing every sweet you also have the sour; and married life is no exception. We knew our share of sweetness and took a long draught of sourness, also.

As it turned out, we two were a suitable match from the start; there was no shirking on the mountain of responsibilities we had to face; work was the daily cross we both had to bear and bear it we did in unity and common understanding. To get through anything worthwhile in life you need co-operation, that yu can't deny; for as we say, 'iron sharpen iron'. Without trust, a partnership is doomed, for truth-be-told you cannot climb with a man you cannot trust.

We had many years of good grace as we embarked upon our journey as life partners up at Five Acres.

Paapa had a vision for Five Acres which he and my ole man, Maas Nat, used to talk about all the while. Although him did buy the place from my puppa some years before, except for my little one acre, he was still respectful towards Maas Nat's feelings about the place. And how the old man must have rejoiced when he came to realise that Paapa and me would splice and keep the land within family circle. Anyway, a portion of it we parcelled off for cultivation by different family members, for is not all of it we did need to be under plantation for ourselves, and a good deal was under lumber-wood.

He was a very self-sufficient man, Paapa, used to working for himself and by now, from time to time, he could offer labouring employment to people around the area, just like my faada before him. Even before we married, he did have his mind set on being him own boss. One thing, him always used to say, 'no talk too much for silence is golden', and that man lived out that motto all his life; I never heard him talking about a matter which he was looking to perform in the future, neither did he utter idle words, for he maintained that Gaad would hold him accountable. If he ever had to talk something of delicate concern or speculation, it would go no further than me and the pillow.

In those days employment was very limited for poor people, that is to say labour work was plentiful but prospects for self-improvement were very limited. You could go out to work on the big sugar estates, work out in a trade or expect to hold the occasional job building government road, church or school, or else doing ground work as a labourer. Still, plenty people would work their own holdings, no matter how it did small. To be poor was never a crime especially when you saw people striving to make something of their lives for themselves and dem next of kin; holding up dem head and giving dem pickney a chance to get a good education and some opportunity to try and prosper. Most of we country people have always struggled to mek sure our children never have to undergo the hard life we were under; always thinking ahead to a better day for those other ones coming up.

Sugar cane

Paapa always used to make sugar, and he had his *cane piece* dem, too. We used to have a whole heap of different varieties of canes in Jamaica. Let me see, there was Wanderer, that was a tough type, Rusty Iron, which come in like the name sounds, hard and tough, Yuba, a next tough one used to mek rum, Black Gold, which was very sweet, Mary Gold, that had a golden colour, Search Island, Stripe cane and Red Neck. There were plenty more: Purple cane, Black cane, Blue cane, Toad-eye cane, Goat-foot cane, Java cane, Cabana cane, Lady Fancy cane, Black woman cane, So-longo cane, me can't remember all.

Growing cane is a hell of a work, man, back-breaking; from planting and maintenance right up to cutting and bundling up to go a mill to mek sugar or rum. It was tough work but it made all who did it tough, too. Blood mingles with the growing of cane, man. Slave labour proved that. Sugar cane is a bitter sweet legacy we have. Yes, sugar sweet, but it bitter too. Bitter sweet.

When the cane is ripe, you would know because it would send out suckers from the base, and the leaves would *heng dung* and look dead. Left longer, the cane would put up its soft white arrow at the top, which some people called 'the flag'. You would then cut the cane very low. If you left it too long to harvest, it could become over-ripe and spoil. But even when the cane was sour you could still use it to make cane vinegar. All you had to do was juice the cane and put it into bottles, cork and leave it to mature in the kitchen, where it was warm, and there it would ferment. You would have to be careful, though, that it wasn't too hot in there, otherwise sometimes you would hear, 'pow!' as the bottle just exploded, or the cork flew out. Even vinegar I made in moderation but the real business was to have a good crop of cane to feed the sugar mill.

Sometimes we used to set the cane fields on fire, and when that happened, you would always hear, 'Sssssss!', the loud hissing coming from the whole heap of snakes in the canefield. This time, the entire field would be on fire so dem no have anywhere to run. At one time, snakes were always in the canefields, along with rats, and if dem did ever bite you, you fart, for those snakes were poisonous. As to the rats, we had to set rat-traps to catch those, although the snakes and the rats used to fight. The two set of vermin were as bad as the other because the snakes used to kill the rats, which used to nyam the cane, although the pair of them were always a problem for growers. You used to have to send in mongoose to destroy these parasites and they would do a good job, but at certain other times you could count on the fire to kill off the rats and snakes, so the workers could get to collect the cane to take to the mill, and the land would be left fallow for a time. Fire also used to treat any cane disease like mosaic which would damage the crop.

In those days, there were two kinds of mills: wood mill and iron mill. Paapa had an iron mill and he did use a mule to pull it. The mill was situated next to the boiling house.

First you would chop the cane, clean it up and bundle it and transport it to the mill; some people would use an oxen cart, mule-buggy or 'foot soldiers' – labourers – to do this. That mill would thresh and grind the cane, pressing out all the juice. It would pass through the rollers several times – the big 'man-roller' and the next two, thrash roller, till every drop of juice had drained out, dry, and collected into the cistern. But even the cane-trash had its uses; we could use it to feed the animals, especially the mule pulling the mill, or we would light a fire under the cane-trash and burn it to make fertiliser, or more time we could burn it like fire-wood.

There would always be a big fire under the copper pots, which we used to boil the cane-liquor; evaporate it and cool it off to make the sugar; one copper was very big (one man alone couldn't manage it), and the other coppers coming down in size for skipping the liquor from one to the next. Someone would stand up by the coppers to watch over the process; stirring the mixture so it didn't burn and skimming off any waste matter or scum from the top as the cane-liquor a boil. Any scum which come off we would use to feed the animals.

When the sugar had boiled down to a syrup, a-bump and bubble, then we added white lime – 'the temper' – to crystallise the sugar. If you continued to boil the sugar a-fire, you could make molasses, that is burn sugar, and it too has many uses, especially for making cake.

The wet sugar we would put into kerosene pans to sell by the quart, pint and half-pint as well as the 'jill cup'. Paapa would often make some sugar-candy called, 'ginger sugar', where he mixed up ginger in the sugar and cut it up into cubes. Big people and little pickney alike use to love that. And we looked forward to drinking the 'copper wash', when it was time to clean out the coppers, or else we would drink pure cane-liquor, sweet and satisfying. Most times, though, we would drink 'beverage' – sugar water with a squeeze of lime juice. That was poor man's wine.

One time, smady set fire to the boiling house while it was stocked up with twenty-odd pans of sugar and other provisions. Through hearsay, we got to understand it was a fellow who owed money for his sugar but never wanted to pay who did start the fire. The damage was so bad, the entire boiling house had to be re-built. Needless to say, the whole sorry episode caused a whole heap a botheration and expense. As for the fire-raiser, police never charged him, so we decided to leave him to Gaad, for vengeance is His.

Rum

Rum cane was always a fine, tough kind of cane; not a very brillant variety. To mek rum, we would use the cane-liquor from the rum cane, distil it, let it ferment and then pass it through the rum-still, leaving it for a good time to mature. We never used to make rum to that, only occasionally, but if we wanted to know if a rum was good, all we would do was drop a little on the table or floor and draw a match stick: it would ketch fire said-speed and burn hot. Anyhow the people who made the rum did add water to it, when you set it on fire, the rum would burn and leave a trace of water same place. If it was the pure spirit, the fire would consume it all.

Jon-crow Rum was a strong rum some fellows used to mek, probably the strongest kind there is and it was contraband. Anywhere that rum dropped, it would stain for how it was strong. Whenever certain men would hear the whisper going round that a consignment of Jon-Crow Rum deh-'bout, dem skin would ketch a-fire with excitement. Pretty soon, gerrey would break out.

Castor oil

I never used to buy castor oil from people, I always used to mek my own. When the oil nut dries, it just pops out. First, we would wash it with ashes water and then parch it in a pot under a good fire, until it was brown, but it shouldn't burn. After that, you put it in a mortar and beat it. While you were beating, you would see the oil coming out. Next, you had to put it in boiling water a-fire and keep stirring till you see a whole heap of oil floating on top. You would have to skim off that first set of oil and then put it in a separate pot to boil, and as it was boiling it will clarify; become very clear and light. To test if it was ready, you would dip in a straw and take up a oil little on it. As you put the straw to the fire, it would ignite, and that meant the castor oil was ready. All there remained to do then was just leave it to cool and funnel it into vials or bottles.

If you were a person who didn't know castor oil, you would be inclined to think it was coconut oil for how clear that castor oil was. We used it all the time as hair-oil to groom hair and to treat belly-ache; as a purgative, and as worm medicine. Most times you would find it selling a' doctor shop, but I made my own and used to carry it go sell a Newmarket where people would comment how it resembled coconut oil. I would tell them, 'yes, is true', but me would warn dem not to go mek mistake and drink it for it will *operate yu*!

Tobacco

Up at Five Acres, we used to grow tobacco. That is something that would grow easily enough and when you see the bottom leaves turn brown, then you knew it was ready for cutting. After that, we would put it out a-sun to let the sun quail it, then bundle it up and hang it above the fire-hearth. When it was dry, it was then ready for making cigars, something I always used to do – through me a did di ole slave who did everything!

Cigars were not a hard thing to make, and it was good quality tobacco we used back in those days. Every one of those cigars were fat, made from the broad tobacco leaves. I took my time rolling and sealing each one with care. After that, I would put them in a simple wooden box to keep them fresh. By the time I had finished, my hands were coloured orange and smelled high, but the odour of tobacco was something I always appreciated. Oftentimes, we used to hear from those men who travelled go a-foreign how Cuban cigars was prime quality, but me know sure that fi-we Jamaican tobacco was sweet and prime too. Whether you were using it for cigars or in a pipe, not a soul had any reason to complain seh a *pyaa-pyaa* bush dem a smoke. Not even the poorest quality Jamaican tobacco could be under-rated. Nuff neaga man would put dem hand 'pon dem heart to declare Jackass Rope tobacco sweet like young virgin.

One time me used to even smoke a pipe. Me mek a little bamboo pipe and when you see me go fi siddung cut me ten, that pipe would always be my companion. After a hard day's labour, I would just settle down, hum and smoke that natural, sweet-smelling tobacco, easing away all the worries on my mind. Or else when you see me siddung and a-consider at certain times, just me and the pipe, you knew you were not to get in my way. It was nothing for a woman to smoke, although some church people never liked it, but man and woman alike would get pleasure from smoking a pipe, yes man. And anytime you asked a little pickney to go light your pipe, they would be so glad because they would get to tek one or two draws off the pipe when you naa look. This time the tobacco was rich and strong, and the smoke could all tear out that chile's nose-hole, him naa complain.

People would come and buy tobacco and cigars from Paapa. He used to sell it by the yard or by the pound when he carried it to market. A whole heap of kufenge used to come buy from him but he was never really into the tobacco growing to any great extent, only from time to time but that was really something to look forward to.

Bee-keeping

I even used to keep bees at one time. Those worker-bees used to travail unrelentingly to collect pollen to go feed the queen. You would watch them, you know, but you don't antagonise them, you would only survey the situation till when time you saw that the hive was fat, then you could go collect the honey – a whole heap of it. But you had to know what to do otherwise the bees would swarm you and sting you up giving you blood poisoning. The first couple of times bees bite you, it hot, but you know, after a certain time it come in like a no nothin', yu hardly noticed it, and your body would build up a resistance to the corruption.

Those bees don't live long, but their short life is very creative and productive.

I used to put up bee boxes to farm honey. I would just erect as many boxes as I liked, placing them high up so nobody could

interfere with them. And you had to know when to go gather the
honey; that is when the bees were finished in a certain area and had
gone off to farm another place. To clean out the boxes, I used to make
sure my head and the whole of me was well-covered over, then I
would light a fire underneath the hive and smoke out the bees. Once
you smoked out the bees, it was not hard to collect the honey and
clean out the boxes. As you took out the frame, you would see it
covered over with the thick honey-comb. Because we were so blessed
with a wide variety of different plants and flowers growing wild all
around; hibiscus, jasmine, tree blossom of many kinds; guava, sour
sop, custard apple, naseberry, dew-plum, and so on, we did get to
produce pounds and pounds of the sweetest honey you could ever
imagine. Sometimes, I would look for the queen bee, see how fat she
was. I would marvel at how she had all the workers at her command
and say to meself, 'fancy!', especially because my life was anything
but fi lady queen's. Inside the kitchen, I would squeeze out the honey
and strain it. I would use the comb which was left to boil for making
wax. All you had do was put on a pot of water a-fire to boil and
throw the comb in it.

A young lady named Emma in the district used to sell wax through
her father used to keep a whole heap of bee boxes. He made a good
living selling his honey in Kingston and all over yonder. As Emma
walked round she used to cry out, 'Waax!', and people would rush to
buy the wax from her to polish dem house. If you never had any wax,
you could use candle-grease to polish the floor, or else you could boil
Salandine and Spanish Needle (which goats eat) and that would be a
good floor wax. Whenever you rubbed it into the wood with the
coconut brush, you could always depend on it to shine your house till
you were all good to slide crass the floor.

Bruk foot

Me did have an aunt named Marian. The story go how one time dem
shine the floor and poor Aunt Marian slide and bruk her foot.

She bawl out : 'Whaaah! Me foot bruk.'

Everybody dropped what dem did a do and run go look. This time,
Maama said Aunt Marian was just on the floor, flat on her back
holding up the broken foot in the air.

Hear Aunt Marian, 'If unno no believe me seh it bruk, unno just shake it and see.'

But she was a rough and tough woman, you know, she never took it too seriously. Everybody else was anxious, but Aunt Marian acted like a pin *juck* her. They bandaged up the foot and told her she 'haffi go a-hospital'. She said, 'Whosh, whosh! Hospital? Fi go do wha'? Same way dem a-go wuk 'pon mi foot, me no can wuk 'pon mi foot to?'

Yam

Hog inna me piece
a root out me minty

Planters like Paapa had a whole heap of choice, for plenty different varieties of yam used to grow in Jamaica. It is no wonder that Five Acres was like verdant pastures; for we had no shortage of crops which the rich, red earth would just prosper and cause to bloom. There was: renta yam, St. Vincent, yellow yam (of which there was two kinds, yellow affu and ordinary Affu) pum-pum yam (this one is round and people seh it feava pum-pum), white yam, which is long an' thin like renta, wild yam, which we used to boil and feed hogs and other farmyard animals, mozella yam, yampi, which was small and long, and the minty coco. Then there was guinea co-co, lefman co-co, dasheen, badoo, all in the same yam family. Yampi was a peculiar type of yam in that whenever you plant yam and it starts to grow, you would place some long poles directly above for the vine to run around. Now, all yam vine runs in one direction, say clockwise. Yampi, now, was a strange fellow: fi-him vine had to run in a different direction to the rest. Even if you set it around the stick in one direction, it would simply unravel that vine and re-set itself.

Once we had planted up, people could stay a distance away and identify which part we had the yam field by the yam hills. Oftentimes, with some varieties, yam seeds would just drop off the vine and start to grow. And there were places where yam would grow plentiful and unattended a-bush land, quite often on property owned by backra which was left neglected or else on crown land; fields full of yam growing and being replenished as the yams yielded their seed to the rich soil year upon year. That time anybody could go and harvest it; a man would say, 'come, mek we go dig old yam'.

You could always tell when yam was ready to harvest for the wiss or the 'vine' would start to dry. But growing yams was only part of the story for we used to cure dem too. During the harvesting, if you were digging up a yam and mek mistake juck it with the machete or digging fork, all you would do is dig out the part that was damaged and rub in some white lime or sour orange, then put it out to sun. When it was dry, you could then put it away in the *butry* or storehouse and the yam would keep fresh for a good year or even longer. To make white lime, you had to build a kiln by piling up some wood cross way each row till it reach about three foot in height, then set fire to the kiln. Most times the wood we used was a tough kind, like 'stone wood' from the bully tree, pimento wood or mahogany. After the kiln burned right through, then rain had to fall on the ashes to melt it down. For us, it had to be rain-water, no other kind. That white lime would serve the purpose of preserving ground food or to 'temper' sugar.

Like our parents before us, Paapa and I respected the land and it rewarded us with an abundance. No wild imagination could ever draw the conclusion that we were rich people because we owned land and a productive sugar-mill; we were only, like so many others, hard-working labouring folks doing what we knew, living within our means. It was as well my buddy charmer and me had managed to get the place under such good control, for little more it wouldn't just be the two of us alone living there and calling it home.

BOOK
2

9
Wings of a Dove

My corner of the sky

Chi-chi-bud-O!
Chi-chi-bud-O!
Some a dem a holler, some a bawl. – (song)

If I had the wings of a dove
said if I had the wings of a dove
I would fly, fly, fly fly, away
and be at rest! – (song)

Ever since I was a child, I loved to watch bird-life; some of those creatures were very beautiful, some dutiful and some very *cunny*. When my load was too hard to bear, I used to daydream about the Psalm which said, 'Oh, that I had the wings of a dove, I would fly away and be at rest'; and I would imagine how carefree life would be if I only had some wings. I would find a corner of the sky and nobody could trouble me. As a married woman with plenty to do, there was never again the chance to skylark; and to dream of being free as a bird.

Not everybody a go understand this, but I always took my inspiration of life from nature all around me; up to now I don't stop marvel yet at how the Creator equips all his creatures. We had so many different birds around the place: grassquit – which lays its eggs in the grass, the ground dove, which makes a sound like, 'me ears a hurt me', that is a duppy bird, jumping dick is a bird that jumps along merrily. The barble dove makes a sound like, 'me plant peas cawn', pea-dove, which makes the sound, 'mary-coat-blue', wood pigeon, blue-belly, quail, and the mighty little picherry – a tiny bird that chases off hawks. There is also the turtle dove, *pilikan*, gaulin, pond coot, parrot, parakeet, fisherman bird, partridge, jon-crow, woodpecker, nightingale, banana bird, *kling-kling*, *patuck*, *gi-me-me-bit*, and of course, the doctor bud (bird):

doctor bud a cunny bud
a hard bud fi dead
yu pick him up, yu lick him dung
a hard bud fi dead.

A certain bird around the place always used to cry out in such a distinctive way that when people heard it they would cry, 'Lawd-a-massy, smady a go dead!' In the same way, another type of bird used to cry in a certain way to let people know that a baby was going to be born.

Aunt Emmie

Not too long after we were married and living up at Rocky Mountain, we had an unexpected visit from my bredda David. He turned up one evening carrying a little baby bwoy of about two.

Hear David, 'Emily, see yu nephew yah.'

I said, 'True?'

He said, 'Yes'.

I never rightly knew whether to believe him or not, for he used to be kind of *jokified*, so I asked him which part him get the pickney from.

David said, 'Who him feava?'

I took a good look at the cute little brown fellow, sweet-smelling and soft like cherubim, then I told David, 'Come to think of it, him really feava yu'.

He said, yes, for it was his son, Benjamin, and he had a little twin sister named Deborah.

This time now David and his wife, Pansy, had separated and it looked like he took away the bwoy and left the girl with her mother, although he always used to carry his supportance go give Pansy. (I got to understand that she had taken up with a next man.)

So now, David had some business to go look after that was taking him out the area, so that is why he left the child with us, but the little man was no trouble whatsoever. By this time we never had any pickney yet, and I will admit, having this young fellow had me brooding before long.

Every morning I would get up, bathe Benjamin, comb his hair, and oil him all over. This time him hair did pretty, you see, straight and shiny like fi coolie; you would just part it at the side and he would come in just like a little sweet man, and the amount of kisses he would receive doesn't bear telling. You could put him down, give him his breakfast and he was as good as ever. When you see that little smady sit down 'pon pony seh him a ride, or else a feed the fowl, you just had to smile; for he was so tiny and intelligent. It was him who christened me 'Aunt Emmie' and from then, the name stuck on, for everybody calls me so right up to today.

Everything was going on well until one early-early morning we got a visit from Benjamin's mother. We never knew she was coming, and the way she turned up so soon and without notice, made me suspicious that something wasn't right. As it turned out, it was bad-minded people who set her to come deh. I even knew the woman who did it, she did name Clementine, and she never liked to see how me and Paapa were living good like husband and wife should live; she would have done anything to mash us up and bring discord into our lives. Lawd, and for how those same people used to love to run go a church! This woman, Clementine, took it upon herself to go and seek out Benjamin's mother and told her bare lies that the pickney was being mistreated and how he was running around the place dirty and a-play with fowl do-do. Naturally, Pansy was concerned and made the long journey at speed up to Rocky Mountain to see her one son. The previous evening, Pansy slept over at Clementine's yard and came up a fi-we yard just as we were getting ready to eat breakfast. As it would happen, the morning of the visit, me did wake up soon and bathed Benjamin as usual, combed his hair and fixed his breakfast. He got a whole crab, big and fat, to himself that morning. So, as the little fellow was tucking into his crab, Pansy came up to the gate and cried out, 'Hold daag'.

I was surprised but me heart never leapt. By now Paapa had already gone a-bush.

I greeted Pansy then asked her, 'What breeze blow yu here now?'

As Gaad would have it she told me everything about the set up and how she even came equipped with clothes to carry Benjamin home with her. But all she could do was stand up and look 'pon the bwoy from head to foot, watch him tucking into his crab and she quickly realised it was a wasted journey. She had even arrived so early with the expectation of catching us red-handed in some maltreatment of the lad, but it was not to be.

When he finished eating, she took Benjamin to one side and talked to him.

'Benjamin.'

'Mam?'

'Yu know me?'

'No, mam.'

'Me is yu madda, yu know.'

'True, mam?'

This time Benjamin no know any other mother besides me, because David took him away from he was a baby and by now he had become fully used to living with us up a-yard.

Anyway, his mother asked him if he wanted to go with her and he told her 'no', he wanted to stay with Aunt Emmie. His beloved Aunt Emmie. Pansy stopped over and spent a little time with us, marvelling over all that her son was doing and how he looked so nice like something you could eat. After about a week, Pansy went back home leaving Benjamin same place, and promising to bring his little sister to come and meet him. Clementine's bad-minded plan had spoiled, but she wasn't satisfied; there were plenty more things she did to try and cause conflict, but it was always she who ended up shame-faced.

I said it already and I shall say it again. A no little me go through wid neaga people; is a whole heap a someting me pass through a'ready.

Midwife

Sister Eleanora – Sa-Elly, as we called her – Paapa's mother, was a well-known nurse in the district. She travelled all over delivering babies and tending to her patients. Now and again she would come up a-yard to look for her son; spend a little time with us, then go back down. One time she paid such a visit, a few months after my faada, Maas Nat, had passed away. They say he took sick and died after dreaming how a black daag did bite him. At that time no amount of consolation was enough for me, for I dearly loved that old man. Still, in the quiet trust I had in Gaad, I gave Ole Natty back to his Maker, and praised Him for His merciful provenance in giving me another good man, in my husband, to take care of me. So, this particular day, as my madda-in-law and me did inna kitchen, suddenly, I became very giddy-headed, the cup in my hand dropped and I nearly collapsed. Well, it was a surprise to me but no surprise to my madda-in-law, for I was pregnant. I never even knew how long, but by her reckoning from what I told her, in five months' time, close to Christmas, I would deliver. Me seh! When Paapa came home the evening, I could hardly look in his face. 'Evening, Mama, evening, Mel, then how is everything?', he greeted us.

'Evening, sah, everything hearty. How yu get on today?' answered his mother.

'Oh, fairly fine. Two a de cows are *with cub* and Ranny Robinson offering to buy one.'

'True? Well that is not bad, but mek-haste go wash yu han' and come for Emily have some more good news fi yu too,' said Sa-Elly.

Well, I made excuses that I did have to go out go pen up the goats but she wasn't having any of it, and made me sit down while she served out the dinner.

'What is it now, Ma-Mel?' Paapa asked when he came round the table.

Me opened me mouth, but couldn't find the right words to speak, so that me started murmuring like dummy till Sa-Elly came to my rescue.

'Son, yu really like having little Benjamin about the place, no true?'

'Yes, mam, him is a jolly lickle fellow, no trouble whatsoever.'

'So he will be a good companion for your own pickney dem, no true?'

'I feel so, mam.'

'So mek me tell yu, it won't be too long for Emily is expecting a baby.'

Well, my good husband nearly dropped off his chair! And for what amount of 'How yu feeling?' he asked me, could fill a book of many words.

Sa-Elly was the midwife for our first pickney, George, who arrived five days before Christmas. I told her plain that she was to tell me everything that she did to deliver babies, for me naa call her up deh again to deliver any more of mine; me same one would deliver them, and that was the way it went. I became my own midwife and delivered seven of my pickney – all except the first one. Not because me and Sa-Elly fell out, or because she wasn't good at her job, Gaad forbid! That blessed lady was more than a mother to me. I only wanted to do it myself; deliver my own pickney dem, for what if me did fall into labour and she couldn't come up in time? It was only when people saw nappy 'pon line they realised that me have baby.

I would tell Paapa when the time had come for me to deliver, and he would help me get everything ready: bwoil up water, sterilise the utensils and so on. He would even put on a big pot of beef and baddoo-bud soup to feed me afterwards. (That soup would make you so strong, and after delivering, I would drink it till me sweat.) But while I was undergoing delivery, I always made him stay out the room till after the baby baan then he could come in and help me fix up everything. I took my time delivering the baby, and then I measured the navel-string. How? I never used an inch-measure, I just used my middle finger to measure the three inches to cut for the navel. The scissors you use to cut the navel-string were not to be used for any other purpose. And there was some strong thread that you doubled and then waxed to tie the navel-string, all that is prepared well in advance and you would even wax it yourself with candle-grease or wax. You made sure you tied that string real good, and then sprinkle some nutmeg around the area to speed the healing; in no time that navel would be completely healed. One time me did just finished cutting off a navel-string when a chicken rushed in the room, picked up the birth-cord and ran away with it. (It must have been devil sen' him in there come do that.) They ran after the fowl and dragged it away before he could swallow it. Looking back, it was really funny but at the time it did cause a commotion around the place.

When new babies baan, you rub their head-middle with horsefititia and they must stay inside for nine days before they can go outside, that is to make sure they don't catch cold or infection. There is nothing like when you hold your own baby in your arms. You just have to look at that little person and consider that it was you who created that; marvel at how such a miracle could come out of your body. You think to yourself, 'what a wonder'. After that, you would find yourself drifting off to sleep, so the two of you would just drop asleep; get some rest and Paapa would come tek the baby from me, place him in the crib. When I woke up, I would tackle that beef and baddoo-bud soup to regain my strength, and set myself up to breast-feed me little poopsie when he awoke.

I used to deliver babies for other people too, but many years later, after I got saved and joined Church of God church, the parson told me not to do it again. He said I should let the people dem go a doctor or else go a hospital otherwise the authorities might have called me 'bush na-na' and prosecute me. But one time a lady named Miss Valda came to me and asked me to deliver her daughter's baby. It was a long way for her to travel go a hospital, you know, for we were country people living far away from the town, and which part Miss Valda lived came in like world's end how it did *fur*. Anyway, she begged me to come and so, I couldn't refuse; I followed her up to the house where the young lady was already in labour. When I went in, the first thing I did was to say:

'Glory be to the Faada, the Son and the Holy Ghost as it was in the beginning and ever shall be world without end. Amen.'

Then I made them bwoil up some water to sterilise what and what me was using; scissors, and such-like. After that I took some warm water and wiped down the young lady's back and front and then turned the baby and started the delivery. All the while I would be reassuring her; telling her when to push and when to rest. In all the time me was delivering babies me never used no doctor book. I learned what there was to learn from my blessed madda-in-law, and just used my head; after all, it is a thing I was around from I was growing up; whether in the fields with the animals or else inna house with people.

Miss Valda's daughter, Blanche, did all she was told and was a good patient. When the baby squealed, its father, Sammy, was frightened so till him mussi piss up himself, so we made him sit down before he did faint and took time laugh after him behind him back. The next morning, him same one would have to go out-a-yard go bury the after-birth and the navel-string. The custom is that wherever he buried them, he would plant a tree same place and the fruit of it would belong to that child throughout its life. And, you know, nature is truly amazing. Say he planted a banana tree; that tree would grow up quite well till it reached maturity, and then, one night – never in the day – one night, you would hear the tree groaning like a woman in labour – groaning, same way like when a mother is about to deliver. The next morning, you would see the navel, or 'banana blossom', as some people call it, on the tree and from that the fruit would develop. The relief and joy of a new birth is quite unspeakable, for those around and for the mother; whether she has only one pickney or one dozen, the miracle remains the same. I told Miss Valda to give her daughter Blanche, the new baby mother, something to drink and told them what and what to give her to eat later on – only something light like soup or banana porridge and to make sure she got plenty of rest. Everybody was excited about the new baby; Miss Valda's face was shining like harvest moon, and the pickney puppa, Sammy, stood up strong like champion bull. Very soon the neighbours were on the veranda a-waiting dem turn to look 'pon Miss Valda's new little grand-daughter. As time went on and the parochial boards became more domineering over matters concerning taxes and so forth, there were always bad-minded people around trying to find out who and who was a 'bush na-na' so they could go tell the authorities and get a midwife like me inna trouble. But Gaad is so good, nothing bad ever happened to me, and all 'my children' are fine, big people who point me out to their own pickney and tell them how it was that I came to hold them before their own mother.

Patchwork quilt

I first started making patchwork quilts when the first child, George, was born. Sewing was something I used to do quite often enough, but it was when I found a use for the scraps of claat that the quilt-making came together. When evening time came, I would gather all the different scraps, cut and trim them nicely and sew them together to make a little quilt for the young baby. Sometimes you should see the pretty colours and textiles we managed to find. Before long, I would get all manner of scraps from friends and family. First of all they used to look at me like me did mad when me tell dem seh a quilt me did a go mek, but after they came and saw how it all joined up nicely all they could do was coo: 'Aunt Emmie, yu no easy, yu can do anyting yu turn yu mind to.'

　　I would just reply, 'Eeh-heeh', for me was never too proud to use scraps to turn into something useful, and what manner of orders never

came for valances, bed-spreads, pillow-cases and what not. If perchance
the wireless was playing, I would just sit down out a veranda with me
sewing until night began to draw in.

Sometimes people who were passing the house would come by
and spend a little time talking and I would entertain the company,
but never once would you see me put down my work; as I would tek
time joining one piece to the next, trim it, neaten it off and all the time
working with patience. Before long, the quilt would be ready and
straight into the baby's crib it would go; covering over my little
poopsie. After a while, I started making quilts for our beds and soon
enough, one of my quilts would be for birthday presents, marriage
gifts, and when time any new baby came into a family, a patchwork
quilt would mark the occasion quite well.

Operation

I remember when I had to go to Black River Hospital to get my
appendix cut. For such a long time I was in agony, but it wasn't until
my madda-in-law Sa-Elly, the nurse, came up a-yard that I found out
the cause was appendicitis. She made appointment for me go into
hospital to get it cut and so I made arrangements for the pickney
dem. The eldest girl, Mary, and George, the first bwoy, went to stay
with Ole Jane, my mother, and from then it was down there they
grew up. You know, many years later, Mary would tell me that me
'give her away like puss pickney'. But Ole Jane did love her and her
bredda too much to make them come back home after I came out of
hospital, and not to mention they provided the help the old lady
needed in her advancing years.

For the operation, Paapa carried me down to Black River, and I
made sure I travelled with my jar to put the appendix in. By this time,
the appendix was so ripe inside me that me could only walk and bend
in pain. Anyhow the appendix did burst inside me, me would-a dead,
so it was a good thing Sa-Elly did come by in time when she did to let
me know what was causing my ailment. At the hospital they told me
the same thing; it was too ripe. A little later and it would have burst.
The day of the operation, I was the second person they operated on.
Before they cut you they give you a wash-out from the night before.
Come my turn, as I lay down, they gave me some chloroform and told

me to count up to ten. Me mussi reach about six and me no remember nothing again till when me wake up. Later, as I looked round, I saw my jar with the appendix in it. A while later still, they gave me a cup of mint tea only, nothing fi nyam till later. I stayed in hospital a good time, and never go back home too soon. And I was no trouble at all so the doctors and nurses loved me, but some of those patients carried on so bad and vulgar the nurses had to slap one or two, but if the doctors saw them ill-treating any patient, they would be dismissed. When I saw that my bandage needed changing, I never bothered to trouble the nurse, I just changed it meself and then pinned it with two latch pins.

When the nurse came along she said, 'Bailey, is who change yu bandage?'

I said, 'Me alone.'

'Nobody helped you?'

I replied, 'No, for Gaad give me the strength to help meself.'

She said, 'Lovely, Bailey, that's right.'

Madda-in-law and the news bug

One time, Sa-Elly came up to stay with us from Monday and she never went back down until Friday. She spent a delightful time around her grand-children, and enjoyed herself quite well. When she left, Paapa carried her as far as Birdsong Fields and made sure she got transportation the rest of the way home. A couple days later, a *news bug* came in the house. I said to to meself, 'I wonder what this means'.

I called Pops – Paapa – and told him to come look, then I picked up the news bug and spat on it. Me tell it seh if it is good news, fly, but if it is bad news me know it would just drop a-floor. Then I threw the bug in the air and it dropped. Tried again, same thing, so we knew there was bad news to follow. A little later, smady carried the news come give us that Sa-Elly was dead. We were shocked so till! Paapa made haste to go down there, but by the time he reached they were just moulding up her grave, so he only got to mourn a little over the burial site and then turned around come back home. Poor fellow, this time it grieved him that he never reached there in time to see his mother for the last time to bid her farewell. As soon as he reached inside the house he started to cry.

I said, 'Hush, man, no cry, for she gaan a'ready.'

Some time later we got to understand how Sa-Elly died. A woman who worked in the same district doing the same kind of work envied Sa-Elly because she had more patients than her. And it was a woman Sa-Elly trained in the nursing business, you know, but she got grudgeful and decided to set something to make Sa-Elly go drown in a sink-hole. Now, Sa-Elly had a little daag, Monty, that always travelled with her and when Sa-Elly went missing, everybody was out searching for her. It was the daag who made the people find where the body was, because that dutiful creature sat down whimpering for his owner by the sink-hole. Even after they bailed it out, the daag decided to stay at that same spot mourning for Gaad knows how long.

You think a yesterday duppy a-walk and you think a yesterday or today bad-minded people deh? A no now wickedness deh 'bout.

Holland Bamboo

Something happened to me one time at *Holland Bamboo*, but as I'm telling it now, I know that plenty people won't believe me. It was the same when I related the story at the time, some people were really doubtful that the incident had really happened as I conveyed it, but, as Gaad is my witness, a no lie me a tell.

A young man in the district named Claudie Steward had undergone a terrible tragedy when his beloved sister, Marlin, died suddenly. The news came as a shock to poor Claudie because, of all the family, it was just him and her alone left and the two of them were close like two gungoo peas in a pod. Nothing was too good for that young woman to give to her bredda; they were raised so loving to one another.

Now, Marlin was only a young woman, she never even married yet and she never had a chick nor child, only her job as post-mistress to worry over. And they say that was the problem, for, according to how the story come to the district, smady coveted the poor gal her job and wuk obeah to make Marlin go dead well before time. She just died all upon a sudden, she wasn't even sick any-at-all. Now that no funny?

Anyway, when poor Claudie heard the news, him bawl so till. As the telegram arrived, that young man heng dung him head and wept!

Plenty times when you hear about death many men wouldn't bawl out loud, they would just hide dem feelings and bawl when nobody naa look, if they bother to weep at all. But this poor young man wasn't ashamed to cry for his heart was truly broken.

Now, Marlin didn't live in the district, she was clear over in Mandeville, how much miles from us? Not two!

Claudie went round asking if anybody could travel with him to go collect his sister's body for burial in the district, for that was where she was born and raised. Not a soul offered to go with him. Some people told him it was too far or that they were under plenty work, but some were honest enough to tell him they wouldn't travel with a dead body in a coffin. That was the real reason. People were too afraid of the dead and, more to the point, they were afraid of duppy.

So, no-one offered to go with Claudie. In the end he sent word to ask if me would go with him. What amount of 'please' he made, I couldn't refuse. This time, he knew me by reputation that I was a lion-hearted woman who wasn't afraid to go and help tend to the dead when anybody passed away in the area. Man, you know it pays to live good, for the name you leave behind you is of more value than silver or gold. So anyway, I told Claudie, yes, I would travel with him to go collect the body of his sister. He was so glad that he hugged me up and what amount of 'tanks' and 'Gaad bless yu', he gave me.

Hear him, 'Tenky me Aunt. The res' a dem people roun' yah a bare fart!'

So we set off. When we were coming back, Claudie sat down 'pon the coffin in the back of the truck. Me dear mah! As we reached Holland Bamboo, the place was flooded right over with water. Heavy rain had fallen, and the place was flooded right over so the vehicle couldn't go through. As we sat there pondering what to do – remember it was a body we were transporting and there was no other road we could use – Claudie started to fret. All upon a sudden, a spotless white bird flew down and sat right down on the coffin. I'm not sure if it was a dove or what, but it was a white, white bird, pure white.

I said to Claudie and the truck-driver, 'This is a sign'.

And, just as suddenly as it had come and sat on the box, the bird flew right off again.

I told them, 'That was Marlin.'

Don't ask me how I did know, it was just the way I felt within my spirit. The next thing that happened, I can only call a miracle. Don't ask me how, but the high water just divided so the vehicle could go through. Divided, I said! As we passed through in the truck, the water just closed right back up again. A no so it did go when Moses divided the Red Sea? Well, the same thing took place at Holland Bamboo that day.

Ever since I was a child, that place was very special to me. I always loved passing through that bamboo grove and used to marvel at how the long, long bamboo trees reached clear up into the air so majestically and just shaded the place right over. It was so quiet and dark in there that you could even forget that outside of the grove, in the sun hot, was broad daylight.

I know that plenty people won't believe that was how the story went. They are quick to disbelieve that the water did really part but they would rather be inclined to believe that such a thing did happen in Bible times when Moses led the Israelites out of Egypt. Yet, after all, it is the same Gaad; He can do anything He feels to do. That was how we got to bring the body back to the district for the funeral.

As the people saw us coming, they started ringing the bell out in the square. The tradition was that when a death is announced, or else when a body arrives for burial, they would ring a bell. Men would always get more rings than women.

So, faithful Claudie got to bury his sister and what tributes they paid to that young woman! Everybody said that pickney gal was truly a Christian. They tombed her at the same time, and when the work was done, as was the tradition, the workers would knock their tools on top of the tomb and sing out, 'tomb finish, tomb finish', then people would just throw some money give them. Claudie did get to mourn his sister properly and laid her to rest. He bear me witness about what took place that day at Holland Bamboo, but we made up our minds that we didn't care who never believed us. If they never believed, that was fi-dem business. It wasn't high praise or gungoo soup we were looking for when we told them about the strange occurence. I am convinced that at certain times, things like that happen so you can just lock it up in your heart and marvel. Marvel at the wonderful and mysterious ways Massa Gaad do His works.

Jack-of-all-trades

There is an old saying, 'cow no know the use of him tail till fly tek him batty', meaning to say that when you are under pressure, you get to find out how resourceful you can be. Hardships made us resourceful; the need to survive and be strong made us manage through even the most testing times and circumstances. I was a shoemaker, midwife, stone-mason, carpenter, seamstress, tin-smith – you name it, I have met the challenge. I even used to make my own graters. Let me tell you how that goes; whenever I used to go to the tin-smith's, I always used to stan' up an watch him at work, especially Maas Elliott, who did have his own shop down by the post office. I would just observe him a good time to see everything he was doing and how he went about his trade. Back at the yard I had some old kerosene pans so I decided to turn me hand making a grater. Nothing is ever too hard once you set your mind to something. I just cut out the two sides of the pan and took a big ten-penny nail to punch holes into it – those were the grater holes which I marked out each one, give it twelve big holes and some smaller holes, using a finer nail, for the coarse and fine grating. That finished, I took the machete and cut the edges the same as how the tin-smith would do it, then neatened it off. After that, I did the same to the other side then bent it over the grater stick and finished neatening it off, ready to use. It looked alright, but the real test of anything is in the doing, so I grabbed some provisions, coconut, corn, carrot, whatever need gratering, and you wanted to see me go to work! It certainly worked well enough, and the pride was all mine for what I had achieved. We used to grater coconuts, squeeze out the juice and then boil it to make coconut oil. The 'custard' from that boiling coconut was very appetising, and we would eat it with food; bammy, roast breadfruit, banana, or use it make *run-dung*. That grater of mine was also good for gratering cassava to make bammy. First, you had to scrape then grater the cassava, wring it out dry, add a little salt and then beat it in the mortar to produce cassava flour. Some people used to sing while they were beating that mortar, but not me; I find that I just worked faster when I never bothered to sing. After you finished making the flour, all there was to do was make the bammies round and to the thickness you wanted then just roast it a-fire. Plenty times we ate bammies for chaclata with fish or with cocoa-tea, but, you could even mix the cassava with ordinary flour to make dumplings or else bake the cassava head and treat it like any other bread-kind.

With all my 'trades' as a jack of all, I hardly have to mention that

I could cook; that was nothing to boast about, for from I was a pickney, and especially because I was a 'girl-chile', I must have been able to cook, there was no two ways about it. A woman couldn't afford to be called 'one-handed' or 'slacky-tidy'; she had to know how to cook, clean and wash well. I went one further and even made the pakis we used to eat out of alongside the china plates which had their place in the cabinet. People would tell me they admired the way I took to all these tasks, but to me, it was never a great thing because I was only acting on whatever need was around the place. In hard times we couldn't afford to buy and more the better that I could apply myself to one handicraft or another. I even made scrubbing boards, baby cribs, rope, hats, patchwork bedspreads, tableclaats, anything at all; I wasn't afraid to try. It wasn't hard to make pickney clothes or under-garments especially drawers but the men of the house preferred to buy their pants and underpants ready made so they used to carry their order to the tailor or dressmaker. All the same, when they did tear, it was me same one who used to have to patch them. From I was just little-bit, I grew up seeing the older people making their own clothes out of crocus-bag, a rough-looking but strong material for making work garments. As for shoes, well, we used to make a type of shoes out of rubber or rough leather which people called 'shupatta'. It didn't look like it did come from any shop and some even used to tek it mek joke, but what did we care? If me turn kufenge – or useless – now, nobody should complain for I have had many trades to my credit, and whether the master of all or merely of some, it was enough for me to try and succeed.

10
Anancy stories

Black anancy

One time *anancy* did bite me. It happened when me was out working in the garden; rooting out and weeding, getting ready to plant some renta yam. I was going on quite cheerily when as me turn so, me see the black anancy. Before me could move or anything, the brute bite me then him mek fi run 'way, and as you see him running, so the poison that him deposit was set to run through me. Me decide me mind seh him naa go get 'way, so I rushed after him and clap him with the machete kill him, and used some of the spider's bottom part, the poisonous area, to rub on where I was bitten; that would counteract the poison. After that I rushed to gather wild-slip wiss and bound it up quickly to stop the poison from getting into me circulation, after that I drank some *bissy*. A bite from that black anancy can give you lock-jaw, so swiftness was of the essence.

Anancy story

From we were children, we grew up hearing all kinds of *anancy stories*. If it wasn't anancy story, it was a Bible story; David and Goliath, how that young shepherd bwoy tek him sling and a stone lick dung the giant who was terrifying the Israelites. Man, we did love that, and after the story we would sing:

> little David play on your harp, hallelu, hallelu
> little David play on your harp, hallelu!

Or else we learned about Samson and the Philistines; how Samson slay those heathens with a donkey jaw-bone but how him 'mek Delilah turn him fool'. Or, we heard about Daniel in the lion's den or else about his brethren Shadrack, Meshak and Abednego in the fiery furnace.

In childhood we used to know those stories by heart and any little pickney could recite such a tale, or else a whole scripture passage like the first or the twenty-third Psalm or else memorise the entire sixty-six books of the Bible and name them one by one in correct order. All that could win you a prize whenever there was a concert or open day at school or church. At home we never had too many books, a dozen or so, but the Bible was our library. Most times, though, people used to just sit down and listen to the telling of a story. Especially in the evenings, when work was finished and everybody had done eat a hearty meal, we would all gather round and *sweet up* the prime story-teller to make him give us a story. One would follow on from the other, and when you have a real good story-teller, then there would be a whole heap o' drama in the telling, for those story-tellers were very masterful; they could make people laugh or even cry. They might have given the listeners some words they had to bawl out at certain times during the tale, or play a musical instrument to accompany it.

Now that I had come of age and was a grown woman with pickney of my own, it was a joy for me to tell such stories to my little ones, and up at our yard most Saturday evenings, when the long day was over and everyone had eaten a good evening meal, we would often have a couple visitors stop by. Before long, the children would be hearing a story. Best of all was Maas Jake Morrison, who had more stories up there in his coco than some who claim to own a bookshop. Usually, I would sit down with my sewing, patching up pants or darning under-garments or whatever, and Paapa would have him newspaper, him Bible or Pilgrim's Progress, but when Maas Jake started, we like the youngsters were just as attentive. And somehow as the story was going on, it was like something just drew people passing by the house to just stop a while, rest dem load and stan' up listen. Before very long, a small crowd would be gathered by the veranda whilst Maas Jake wove his tale like anancies love to weave their webs.

Bra' Anancy and the magic cooking pot

Hear Maas Jake, 'mek me tell yu about Bra' Anancy an' the magic cooking pot. Unno ready?'
Everybody: 'Yes, sah.'
Maas Jake: 'Unno sure?'
Everybody: 'Yes, tell it!'

Maas Jake: 'It goes like this: one time, long ago, Bra' Anancy leave him yard vex. Him did quarrel wid him wife an' after him done trace her, him kiss him teet' and stormed out. Dis time now hungry jus' a lick him for him never have any breakfast. Nothin' never deh a yard fi nyam; a dat him an' him wife did a argue 'bout. In fact the whole family was hungry for food was rationed because a famine was on the land. Which part Anancy lived, no food was to be found at-all, at-all. Barely any co-co or yam or breadfruit did a-grow. Tings were very rough, but Anancy was so mean dat him decide fi go see what him could find to eat fi himself alone. So this particular day, him set off to look what fi full him belly. As him a walk now, hungry jus' a cry out inna him belly an' him mout' corner a get white inna the sun hot. As him was walkin', him see wan pot siddung by the road-side. Him run quick go see if any *bickle* did in deh.

As him open the cover, the pot said, 'Call me "Any Food Of My Choice".'

Anancy heart leapt an' him stepped back.

Hear him, 'A wha dis!' The pot could talk. Again the pot said the same as before. Though him never quite believe, Anancy called out: 'Any Food Of My Choice, me waan' some run-dung wid yam, sweet pitata, bru'fruit an' bwoil plantin' an' some beverage fi drink.'

As him seh so, all the food appeared inside the pot.

Anancy said, 'Kiss me neck!' an' then him *wax off* the whole a it. Him even lick out the calabash, then when him finish, him siddung side-a the pot an' smiled to himself. Hear him, 'Bwoy, a so life a go sweet from now on! Me naa go wuk again, an' like how famine is on the lan', yu will mek me very rich.' And him patted the galley on the back.

After he finished resting, he got up an' took up the pot.

Hear him: 'Come mi frien'. Yu a go help me enjoy life from now on.' When Anancy reached home, he took time look roun' fi see who an' who was about. When him no see no-body, him tek time sneak inna the yard and go inna room. Him shub the galley under the bed an' threw some of his belongings over it to hide it good.

When-time him wife an' pickney dem come in from the fields he asked dem, 'Unno get anything fi eat?'

Dem tell him 'No, only one small-small breadfruit an' two lickle finger a banana'. The wife cooked dem an' shared it roun' as bes' she could. Anancy helped dem eat it off den everybody go a-bed.

When dem a sleep, Anancy get up an' took out him pot. Him call out the magic name,'

(Everybody: 'Any Food of my Choice')

Maas Jake: 'That's right, food appeared an' him nyam off every drop. Next day, him gwaan like nothin' never happen, get up an' tell dem him going to look food. Dat evening, the wife cooked the bare so-so scrapses she and the pickney dem did manage to find like before, an' everybody go a-bed still hungry. In the night, Anancy get up again an' order him food from the magic pot. As him was eating, the food sweet him so till him never see that the youngest pickney, Fanso, get up because him did waan' wee-wee. But as the chile see him father a-eat, him decide fi jus' li-dung an' act like him a sleep, while him peek 'pon him *craven* puppa.

The next day Anancy get up as usual seh him a go look food, which, by the way, him never ever manage to find! This time now, the res' o' the family looked drawn an' maaga while Bra' Anancy looked fat an' lively. Only lickle Fanso knew why. When him did certain seh him puppa gaan, him run quick go under the bed an' tek out the pot. Him bawl out what him did hear him father seh in the night and same way food appeared. The pickney an' dem mother did so glad, dem eat dem belly full. When dem done, the mother shake her head an' said, 'Unno father really *logie*, look how him have dis wonderful pot an' keep it to himself. No mind, we wi' play him at him own game.' She tell the pickney dem not to say a word an' den she took the pot go wash it, put it back which part dem find it. Dat night Bra' Anancy tek out him beloved pot, an' call out whe him always call out, but nothin' happened. Him call out again, but no food no come. What is dis? Him look good 'pon the pot an' realise seh smady wash it an' it stop working. Him climb inna bed vex and never sleep a wink the whole night.

Next day, him set off soon-soon determine fi go find a nex' magic pot. Him walk along an' him see wan long stick lean up against wan tree. As him approach, the stick call out: 'Beat-me-hot, Beat-me-hot.'

'Aii!', cried Anancy, glad now because him feel him find something good.

Him cry out after the stick, 'Beat-me-hot, Beat-me-hot.'

All upon a sudden, the stick get up an' start beat Anancy till him cry out an' him body start bruise up. Him bawl out to the stick fi stop, but it never stop. As him a run from the stick an' it a follow, a-beat him, Anancy see wan cow.

'What me fi do?' he asked the cow.

'No tell it "stop". Yu fi tell it "Tan-deh", said the cow.

So Anancy cry out, 'Tan-deh' and the stick stop beating him an' stan' up same place. Anancy decide to tek it home. Him still vex about how him family go interfere wid him magic pot an' mek it stop work, so him decide fi teach dem a lesson. When him go home, him hide the stick under bed. Him mek sure Fanso and the other pickney dem see him a do it.

Next day him set off soon-soon, but him no go far. Him only hide in some bushes overlooking the house fi see what an' what a go happen. As him gaan the wife an' pickney dem go under bed go tek out the stick. The stick seh, 'Beat-me-hot, Beat-me-hot,' so dem mimick it. As dem do so, the stick get up an' lick the whole a dem all over dem body. Dem bawl out fi the stick stop, but it beat as hot as ever. Anancy stood up out a door a-see what a gwaan an' a laugh. After a good while, when him was ready him go in an' tell the stick fi 'Tan-deh', so it stop beat.

'Dat will teach unno no fi trouble me tings', him tell dem.

Dat sly Anancy never consider seh him should take the pot home go share wid him family, no. A so him did *gravalicious*. Anyway, while the mumma and pickney were banding up dem bruises, Bra' Anancy took the stick an' chop it up wid him machete. Him tek up the pieces go throw dem away in the river. The river carried dem out to sea and swept them abroad; all over the world. An' me tell yu, Jack Mandora, that is why any which part yu go a-foreign, yu will always find stick which people use to beat dem pickney.'

By the time Maas Jake finished the story, everybody was feeling good and elated. Those of the children who were still awake, would be calling out for another story, while those who had fallen asleep would be carried off to bed. And despite their whining, the other ones too would get their marching orders, for the big people themselves wanted to hear stories of a different kind. Before long, the talk would be about those who 'dead an' gaan but come back' – duppies.

11
Duppy

The dead and the living

There are plenty of duppy stories, and the more of them you hear, the more leave to tell. Duppy stories go back from before Wappy kill Filope. That is to say, they have always been around. Apart from everything, they are just part of our culture and tradition. Many people have it that duppies don't exist. They say is people imagine such things or else they have if as a joke that spirits of the dead can really be amongst the living. Some even say that it's only ignorant or 'fool-fool' people who could pay mind to such things. That's alright. If people want to believe that, a fi-dem business. Me know what me see an hear already, and no imagination nor fun no in it. Duppies are real, alright, as real we of corruptible flesh.

When smady dead, you lay them to rest. A sleep dem a-sleep till the judgement. The last words the parson will pronounce over the dead person is 'rest in peace'. That mean to say they no have no place amongst the living again. Their time of work and sufferation and pleasure on this earth is over and their spirit is to be at peace. But for all that duppies are still about, and often what you would hear about them were wicked things; for they would frighten or harm people, tief away young children, drive people mad or even kill. Duppies are restless souls; the spirits of people who used to live bad in life, or of people who died in an ill-fated way, or even of people who used to do foul deeds and never confessed before they died; they behaved like demons in life and afterwards they were hell's own. In life and in death they refused to move towards the light; that is, righteousness.

Spirits no have any business fi a-walk up and down troubling people and making mischief. Most times it is wicked people working *kacoma*, that is witchcraft, who set duppy 'pon people to make their life hell. Or else yu would find certain restless spirits roaming the place or else hooked up in a house trying to drive out the living from there. That is the same way it happened with a lady named Miss Joycie over in Mucum Valley. Smady set duppy 'pon that poor woman, and for twelve good years it haunted her to the grave. As soon as night came people reported that they could hear her a bawl blue murder how the duppy, Gruppa, beat her, all carry her up in a tree; throw her into the fire; fling bwoiling water 'pon her. Whenever people would go to the house, the duppy would stone them, right down to the parson, so till everybody else left the yard except for Miss Joycie. All the try she tried, she couldn't get no peace; her life was a living hell till she dead. Any way you look at it, duppies are not a good thing, for the dead have no business with the living. Still, same like how you have good people, bad people, ignorant people, wicked people, the same way you have different kinds of duppies. Coolie duppy always have a reputation as one of the hardest duppies to overpower; *dem no ramp*. From we were children, we used to listen duppy story. That time everybody would be locked up inside the house and no matter how we wanted to pee-pee, it either had to wait till daylight or else we would use the chamber pot under the bed, for we dare not leave the house to go use the latrine.

From we were the size of a grasshopper, we had heard that there was the Rolling Calf, the wickedest kind of creature that would roam about on the blackest of nights when the moon was young, with a loud noise like pure hellment and with fire in its eyes and as it walked, balls of fire would drop out on the ground. Some people reported how they have heard the chains rattling and trailing behind the beast, and heard the grumbling, 'moon walk-i yonder, come out-i yonder'. Next day when you passed the area, there would always be a strong-

strong smell of sulphur heavy in the air and scorch marks on the ground. Heaven help you if you were out at night in the path of a Rolling Calf; woe betide! For even if you lived to tell it, you wouldn't have any sense left. They say at certain times, Rolling Calf would sleep by the roadside and when you pass there the place would be as hot as ever. They do say it is the wickedest demon out of hell which comes and walks the earth as a Rolling Calf. I have heard the chains already and felt the heat as they have passed by, so me naa say a lie people a tell when they say anything at all about those terrible duppies. Three-legged Horse was another demon. That duppy must have been a horse which used to pull a hearse, and when him dead he came back as Three-legged Horse. The noise he makes goes, 'itty-itty hap' as him a gallop about the place at certain times near the end of the year disturbing people's animals. And he was said to be very quick and could run faster than any four-legged horse. Anyhow you see him coming, run under wire – fast. If you jump over the wire, he would jump over too and kill you, but him can't reach under wire.

Another duppy we heard about was the Whipping Bwoy duppy which hoops and hollers, and if he catches you, he would blow bad breeze 'pon you, and that would cause sickness and death. We even used to hear certain talk bout how some duppies were blood-suckers, like Kin-Owl or Kreech-Owl which flies in the dead of night seeking whose blood it could drain. At nights, when we heard the patuck crying out, 'a-whoooo!', as children we would always wonder if it was kin-owl, and run to hide under the bed. Now, I would smile to myself as I observed my own pickney doing the same.

Duppy punkin

Close to home we had experiences of duppies' involvement in people's lives. The story goes how even Peter, my husband, did get bitten by a duppy when he was a pickney bwoy of about seven.

One day, while the family lived over at Mount Vale, his mumma, Sa-Elly, went to market while he and Jethro, his bredda, were in the woods playing. They mussi did a race or a-look birds with their sling-shot, me no know, but as they were skylarking, Peter out-ran Jethro and reached an old boundary wall. There, he saw someone calling out to him: 'Come mi pickney, come.'

Lawd-a-massy! this time a duppy, yu know!
As Peter went to the person, the duppy ketch him and bite him on his arm then take him away over the wall. When Sa-Elly returned from market, she asked which part Peter deh. Nobody no know. Jethro, now, did hear when the person had said, 'Come mi pickney, you a mi pickney,' although he didn't see anyone, but he told them what had happened.

They ran quickly go call a man named Doctor Campbell. He had a reputation as someone who was not afraid of duppies and he could see dem, too. So, Doctor Campbell came and everybody set out searching for little Peter.

Eventually, when they found him, just as the night was closing in, it was way up in a silk cotton tree that the duppies had put Peter to siddung. At the same time the duppies were in the tree keeping watch over the bwoy.

From we were children, we always used to hear how it was in cotton trees duppies live, so we never used to play around those trees at all.

When he sighted Peter, Doctor Campbell pointed up at the tree and told the duppies, 'A him me come fa.'

Then he climbed the tree to go collect the pickney and tek him home. When they reached the yard, they took Peter, bathed him and rubbed him down with salt-water and lime. This time they had to keep watch around the house the whole night because the duppies were bound to come and try to claim Peter back. They must have loved off the little bwoy on account of how him was cute and fat. Anyhow the duppies did get him for any length of time, they would have fed him with rotten wood and *duppy punkin* for that was duppy food. That is what they would use to keep him with them for all time; any living person eating that kind of food would soon perish. Doctor Campbell knew what to give Peter to restore him back to good health and told everybody what they had to do to make sure the duppies never returned to steal him away during the night, for that was their way. So, for two or three nights, the family kept up a vigil and burned rubber out in the yard till the duppies stopped coming back to the house. Anyhow they did get that child, he would have been finished. Back in those days duppies always used to take away people pickney. A no lie. And from they chose Peter and bite him, that meant they really wanted him.

And to the day he died, Peter still had the mark on his arm where the duppy woman did bite him.

Duppy conqueror

And, you know, it is the same way duppy did try to thief away Ma Fanny, my grandmother, when she was still a girl.

Now, you should know that in the olden days duppies were really fierce creatures and so strong you couldn't imagine. They were a wicked set of brutes that always used to abduct children, and some people who practised black magic and were well into the black art book, would sell children to the devil. Duppies would steal those youngsters away. They would simply vanish, never to be seen again. You could search from here to Kingdom Come, you would never clap eye 'pon them again.

It was around Christmas time and Ma Fanny had gone on an errand for her mother. After she made the delivery, she stopped over to play a while and enjoy some egg-nog which the lady of the house had freshly made. While she was drinking it, some of the nog threw away on Ma Fanny's garment.

Well, the time came for her to leave and make her way home, and so she set off. But, as she started going along, some duppies caught the scent of the egg punch on her clothes and started following her. I imagine they must have been saying to themselves, *'whe' fi-me deh?'*

So anyway, Ma Fanny was going along quite contently, when all upon a sudden she heard a voice telling her, 'come', and she must have followed it for she went missing three whole days; not a soul knew where she was in that time but they raised the alert and sent out a search party. It was some people out working dem ground who found her. She was caught up in some *brial* and looked wild with her eyes glazed over, staring straight ahead but not seeing a thing; and she was very afraid like she wanted to run away from people.

The duppies were feeding her with rotten wood and duppy punkin, duppy food, and all she could say was, 'Maaah!' like she was a goat.

The people who found her asked her what she was doing there, but all Ma Fanny could say was, 'Mi no know, a wan woman tell mi fi siddung for she did a go get feeding fi me.'

They had to hold her tight and carry her home where they rubbed fine salt in her mouth and then bathed her down, rubbing her all over with lime and set up a prayer meeting. But, that night, all hell broke loose around the house for the duppies came back to re-capture Ma Fanny. It was pure duppy grumbling going on around that yard, unsettling the animals and humans alike. Finally, someone inside the house cried out, 'a no fi-unno pickney, a fi-we chile.'

Back in those days, duppies were really bare-faced. It is only since vehicles like trucks and motor cars are running up and down that duppies tek flight, because they can't stand the gas and light that the vehicles give off. But in the olden days they were very bold and six-o-clock a evening-time couldn't catch young children out of door, otherwise duppies would try to take them away for sure. After Ma Fanny suffered that experience of being abducted, she couldn't eat a thing, they had to try and force her, and even then her food had to be very salty. It was a whole heap of work they had to do to put her back to rights, to tame her, because after a week she was still carrying on wild. In the end she did get better, but more than that. For when she grew up, is she same one who turned around and chased off duppies when they came to trouble people. So much so that they used to call her, Duppy Conqueror.

In her adult life Ma Fanny used to raise hogs. She had some she was fattening to go sell. So she set about feeding the hogs with corn to fatten them, taking care over their diet and maintenance but smady coveted her and set contaminated meat for the hogs to eat. After that duppies came and started provoking the hogs, so the animals were grunting all the time and wouldn't settle. This time Ma Fanny used to be able to see duppies; ever since the experience she'd had as a girl. The duppies would come and provoke the animals but whenever she went outside, they would run away. As soon as she went back inside, they would come back troubling the hogs, causing dem to rail. So Ma Fanny went and grabbed a cowskin whip which she did tar and set down by the doorway. She palmed the whip and beat after those demons. Now, they do say that from you can see duppies they can't harm you, and she used that whip to drive them off, but they would tek time come back every now and then. In the end, the duppies never stop disturbing those animals till she sold them off and gave up raising hogs. See how bad-minded people stay?

They set out to wreck Ma Fanny's livelihood all because of jealousy. Now, not one word of that story is a lie or the work of imagination. Duppy interference is part of life, and who feels it knows.

Story night

Maas Jake and his bredda Melville knew more duppy stories than anybody else, and they could tell them in a way that tied up your attention and caused the weak-hearts amongst us to feel fear and trembling. After the telling of the anancy stories, some of the by-standers would depart up or down the hill, some saying they would soon come back. Even some of the youngsters who we sent off to bed would sneak back to listen duppy story and imagine we never noticed them keeping ever-so-quiet in the background along the floor. But you know, what really got the duppy talk going in the first place, was a mention by Ruthie Graham that she did parch some *cawn* earlier in the day and how she would go bring some come for everybody to share and enjoy. Well, as soon as she said so, out came Nancy Pettifer with, 'Me hope yu remember fi puddung de duppy share for yu know dem have to get dem feeding whenever time yu parch cawn.'

So Ruthie tell her 'That is ole time story and nothin' no go so.' Well, what an eruption there was on the veranda! Everybody talk same time tell poor Ruthie she better go put out some for the duppies or else they might come terrorise her in the night, for duppies love parched cawn and anyhow you made it, they had to get their share or else. In the end Ruthie was not a little perplexed, and said she would soon come back for she had a matter to attend to and then she would bring the parched cawn come. She left said-speed along with Jasmine Whithorn and her brother Justin, who said he was going to come back in a while with some ginger beer. Old Man Clancy, who did turn dummy after his mule kicked him in him head twenty years before, came by with a bottle of rum and some old cigars that did stink to high heaven, so they made him go smoke a little way off and when he finished he could come back and tek his place on the veranda. Where more rum came from, I don't know, but rum, cake and even a couple or more breadfruits, some ackees and a healthy-size piece of *baccalow* appeared, and pretty soon, they were roasting merrily on a fire which Paapa set up just over to the side o' house; it wasn't worth the trouble to go round the kitchen, for the story-telling and the food could cook along together, and the fire would warm the listeners as the enclosing night would turn more and more chilly.

Before long, Ruthie hastened back carrying a big bag of parched cawn and some sour-sop juice.

Hear Maas Melville, taking the bag from her, 'Now Miss Ruthie, is plenty yu have here. Yu sure any leave up a' yu yard?' Some started laughing.

Miss Ruthie replied, 'Yes, sah, is plenty me did mek, yu know, but more still leave inna kitchen.'

And then Maas Melville countered, 'Good, for yu never know when yu can expec' company, no true?', and those who could understand his meaning gave a laugh and nudged each other surreptitiously in agreement while Ruthie quietly took her place on one of the steps by the veranda. Before long, all who said they would return also arrived, their errands completed and their offering bestowed on the gathering. Any others remaining, or having the inclination, could come by when they would, for the long night was still in her infancy.

Skin-a-mi

Maas Jake's mout'-corner bounced up and down like a woman's *bubby* as he ate a calabash of parched cawn, pausing only to sup some juice to help along the dry morsel. He knew everybody was waiting patiently on him, but he also knew how to stoke the fire of our anticipation whenever he was story-telling. When he was ready, his bright eyes took on a far-away look, then he began,

Ole witches always live amongst people. Dem look the same and even act the same as ordinary folk. Only ting, a' night-time the witch will tek off har skin an' go out de yard roaming go look people blood fi suck out. Most often, is young pickney blood dem prefer. Ole Ma Larry was such a brute who did live over Fruitful Vale. She used to roam at night and climb in through the winda or through the shutter when everybody was sound asleep, an' go suck the blood of a person who was sleeping. When she done, she would fly back to her yard an' as she reach in the room, the witch would bawl out, 'Skin-a-mi', an' then climb back into har skin. Some had it she would cry out, 'fit skin fit' or else, 'kinny-kinny-a-mi', all the same, the ole hige used to put on back the skin and carry on as before. A couple days later, dat young pickney or big person whose blood she suck would-a sick, sick, like him anaemic an' before yu know it, dem would-a dead. They say the only way fi ketch dat ole witch was to tek time go to har yard while she had off har skin and gaan then yu would go full up the skin wid salt. When the witch reach back an' go fi climb in the skin, the salt would burn out har *warrawarrahit!* She would-a dead same time. Is the same way dem did ketch Ole Ma Larry but she was not the last, oh, no. Even today yu still find Skin-a-mi living side by side ordinary people calling out 'howdy-do' every morning. Quite often, it is the last person yu would suspect. Only time will tell.

Maas Jake finished and looked around at each face going up close to each one. As he got up to Ruthie Graham, him go so, 'Boo!' and everybody jumped, especially Ruthie, but while we enjoyed the laugh she told him no fi do so, for her heart couldn't tek too much excitement, at which we laughed all the more. Man, as children we used to hear about 'Skin-a-mi' and how it would terrify us young pickney, and whenever we used to misbehave, the big people would warn us to behave or 'Skin-a-mi' would come tek us away. That warning would blow one time only and we would all behave so good you would believe we were angels.

Maas Jake continued to talk about some duppies which live a' river called River Mumma or in ponds named Pond Mumma. He said:

That kind is a witch that would drag people under the water. One time there was a young gal who saw a woman in the river a-comb har hair. It was a witch but the gal never know. When she see the gal, the woman rushed under water and leave her pretty comb behind. The gal tek it carry home, but in the night the river mumma dream to the gal seh she fi bring back the comb or else she would come kill her. Early the next morning, the gal fly down to the river so fast go throw the comb in deh. So, the moral of the story is if yu ever go a pond or river bank and see something valuable, leave it same place for it could belong to a witch and no matter who yu are or where yu live, dem wi' find yu.

Maas Jake finished and helped himself to a piece of cake and a handful of coconut drops. While he ate, everybody talked, for each of us had our own duppy story to impart to the gathering, but as yet, the master story-teller was still warming up.

As for me, I knew that duppies could be very familiar but me and dem wasn't *wrenkers* nor combolo. Whoever or whatever they were, spirits, ghost, living-dead, demons, the best thing they could do was haul dem arse *kirrout*. What dem a do yah? It is not here they belong, dem fi go back which part a hell dem come from. As we waited for Maas Jake to finish, we heard who and who duppy did follow or trouble, who set duppy 'pon who, which part fi mek sure we no walk and what to do if a certain time of night caught us out of door to mek sure duppy no trouble we. Marion Grant said that as a child, her people warned her that if she 'get up early morning an' a walk out and saw a man or woman she no know who call out, "mawning", she no fi answer for it could be a duppy and anyhow she answered, it would thief away her voice and might have even tek her 'way too'.

'Well, that is common knowledge', said Nancy Pettifer, 'and again certain people used to seh if yu feel duppy a-follow yu, yu should tek off yu clothes an' put dem on back to front, or else turn round an' walk back-way whe' y'a go,' to which there was hearty agreement or an alternative suggestion from Miss May Pinnock who was in the superstition so deep that she would always 'tu'n-har-roll' as soon as she reached her gate and then walk backwards straight up to her house; and if she threw out water a' night-time, she would clear her throat and cry excuse to any duppy family she had standing outside so the water wouldn't ketch dem.

'Yes, is true', said Miss May, 'an' if duppy inna room an' no waan' leave, yu should put out a inch measure – for remember is dat dem tek measure dead body. The duppy would leave quick-quick for him no waan' get measure twice'. 'Yes, yes', everybody nodded, for that was quite well-known.

'An' if duppy a chase after yu, when yu reach a crossroad, simply tek out a knife an' stick it the ground an' the duppy would have to turn back, for they can't go any further,' offered Marion.

'Or if duppy a follow yu, throw down a handful of rice at the doorway an' the duppy will have to pick up every single grain, one by one and count dem. If daylight catch dem, they would have to go back to the place of the damned,' Marion added.

'Ole time people seh if yu go a doctor fi medicine, yu should put English cork in the top of the medicine bottle and then put a needle inside the cork to stop duppy from troubling the medicine', said Nancy, and Miss May told everybody it was so.

Only two people disbelieved, Linbert Taylor and Nehemiah Blake who laughed after Miss May and Nancy, and not to mention poor Ruthie who by now did look frightened as can be.

'Unno can laugh, but a no lie. Every new-baan suckling can tell yu how it is that duppy live inna cotton tree and how they eat rotten wood an' duppy punkin. As for paw-paw trees, that is another place where duppy live. Yu no fi plant paw-paw tree too close to your house for the duppies will draw out the life of whoever lives there, or else they would stone the house', said Miss May but Linbert and Nehemiah still carried on with their rum laugh, which, no doubt, was to ease dem nerves.

Duppy feeding

Nancy took up the bag of parched cawn and poured out some.

'Beg yu lickle waata,' she said to Nehemiah, knowing he would have to go round the back by the kitchen by himself in the dark. 'Me know for a fact dat duppy love parched cawn for from we a did pickney, anytime mama parched cawn, as soon as night come, without fail yu would hear the duppy dem inna kitchen a-beat dem mortar and the pots dem a rattle. A bare laughing an' talking yu would hear going on same like inna day when the same work was happening. Some people who were doubtful, would seh is rat or daag, but no sah! Dis time the kitchen did lock up an' me know sure seh rat an' daag can't talk an' laugh an' beat mortar,' Nancy said, 'Nex' morning when yu go look inna kitchen, everyting would be covered up good an' clean as how it did leave from the night before. If a lie me a tell, Massa Gaad wi' strike me dead,' Nancy announced, crossing herself, before reminding Nehemiah she needed the water to drink so that the parched cawn wouldn't *clide* her. The young man acted bravado before he got up and stumbled round to the back in the dark till smady called him and offered him a bitch lamp telling him,

'Me know yu can see in de dark but tek dis all de same and if yu go see anyting untoward, jus' holler an' we will rush come,' to which Nehemiah kissed his teeth and grabbed the lamp. We heard him singing loudly to himself and cussing as he filled up the pitcher, and, two twos, he was back by which time Miss May was talking how it is that some people *kibba up* food to feed duppy.

'Dem have it seh a feed dem a feed the duppy so it can protect dem from harm or fight off bad-minded people or malicious duppies. When yu feed duppy so, it would come in like a member of de family. Dem might even think dat the duppy is a member a dem family who dead from way before and come back. Some might claim to see de 'person' or they might smell a certain smell dat match somebody dem did know who dead, or else the duppy might reveal certain characters which mek dem feel a fi dem frien' or relation. Some all go get read-up a' *balmyard* an' might hear that such an' such spirit deh wid dem, so dem liable to tek dat fi good luck an' do dem bes' to accommodate the spirit. Some have it seh dem dream such and such a person whe dead and how de person dream to warn dem about danger or else dream some good luckied news to dem, a no today all these things a happen,' Miss May said.

'So tell me someting, when dem put down food to feed duppy, is who eat it?' asked Linbert.

'Yes, who but the same people inside that house,' said his spar Nehemiah, 'an' then dem seh is de duppy eat the food.'

'Another ting again,' said Melville, 'anybody can say what happen if dem ever stop feeding those duppies?' Some laughed, and everybody looked at Miss May for the answer.

'Unno no bother look 'pon me for me never feed duppy yet, so me no know how it would go if dem stop get dem feeding,' Miss May said, becoming vexatious. 'Well, I heard about a man over St. Elizabeth who used to do such tings, and by and by he became very prosperous. Anyway, he decided to get married and when the wife came, he told her all she was to do. Every morning she was to put half dozen eggs inside a pot in a corner of the kitchen, but she was never to look inside the pot and it was never to be washed by her. All was going along fine, till one day the woman tek a stock of the situation and decided she gwine start sell the eggs, and eventually curiosity made her decide to find out what was inside the pot she was feeding so every good day. When she tek off the pot cover and peeked, a dutty big snake with two heads jumped up after her. She ran out that house so fast and it rushed after her to kill her. She ended up inna *Belvue*,' said Maas Jake, and that caused many a shudder amongst the gathering.

Finally, Old Man Clancy began to murmur but nobody could interpret what he was trying to say, so they called for a pen and paper so he could write, and so, in a scrawl that looked like pickney drawing, he set down his opinion that duppy feeding is a covenant people enter when they want to obtain riches but all that is vanity.

'There is always a price to pay, for Satan never give something for nothing,' Old Man Clancy scribed, and everybody spoke up in agreement while the old man took up a fire-stick to light up one of his stinking cigars. We heard the tinny music coming from down the hill, a long way off while young people passed by on their way out to dance, as the dark clouds rushed past the bright moon face. For all we know, duppies were passing by too, or standing up same place listening to our tales. A youth named Percival passing on his way down to the dance, stopped to greet us.

'We a chat 'bout duppy, yu no 'fraid?' Miss May asked him.

'No, mam, for duppy know who fi frighten,' the young man replied and imparted some of his own personal experiences of ghostly encounters before skipping off to join his fellows.

As for me, is plenty testimonies me hear about how people see duppy. Sometimes you would get a report of how someone who had died was seen walking in the district. When the witness looked good or else called their friend to come look, the person would just disappear or else they would *change into a dog* or another animal.

'This is the plain truth,' said Justin, 'Crass my heart this is a true story for one time me was going over Manny Gully to do a little carpentry work for Miss Agnes and me tek short-cut up by Mount Pleasant. All of a sudden me could hear some people a sing, so me believe is a digging match in de bush and as me get closer, me sight a group sitting down round a big fire; men, women, pickney. Me go fi call out to dem but as me get closer fi go greet dem, fire go out and all singing suddenly stopped. There was not a soul to be seen, and not a sound more. Me start wonder if me did a go mad but from me reach down a Miss Agnes and talk the story, she and plenty more confirm seh dem see or hear the same ting or else dem heard about it already. Me a no smady whe frighten easy, but after dat day it was a long time before me travelled that way again.'

Justin's account put Nancy in mind of an old time song, so she strike up:

> If yu waan 'fi hear how duppy laugh
> go dung river-side early morning.

Man duppy laugh 'ha-hiiiiah'
woman duppy laugh 'ke-ke-keng ke'

After she finished, everybody begged her not to sing again for her quavering voice sounded too harsh at that time of night and they feared she might go wake up the entire district, but Nancy kissed her teeth and said she wanted to tell a story too. Eventually, Maas Jake agreed, saying, 'Let peace reign in Israel' and so Nancy got her turn as duppy story-teller.

Talking cow

They say when young green banana leaf drops off a tree on a sudden, it means smady a go dead. And again, when time yu hear a cow is moo-ing day and night, that is known as 'talking cow', and the beast would be digging its foot into the ground non-stop. The meaning is very simple; it means someone is going to die. A prophesy the cow a prophesy, and all who was hearing it would cross themself and pray it wasn't them. Whenever the noise of the cow got too much for some people, for they feel that 'dem corner dark, they would go cut out the cow's tongue.

Kaul

People who are born with a 'kaul' and certain daags – dogs – that have four-eyes could always see duppies. When a child is born with kaul-fat, you had to know what to do. Kaul-fat comes in like goat's fat that you get at the butcher. It is a thin, pink piece of membrane covering over the baby face when it is just born. When a child is born with kaul-fat, you would know they were kind of special. You would tek time peel off the tissue and hang it out to dry. Then yu would parch it and pound it, after that you would sprinkle it over food to eat, or else drink it. Only members of the family were to partake of that, not outsiders. The kaul-fat isn't something you should throw away or bury like the after-birth. The kaul-fat is something delicate and has a special treatment to it, so you would just follow the tradition. As for the person who was born with that, they are very gifted and often-times would be able to discern spirits. Daags that have four-eyes were a good thing to own because they would protect your life and property from intruders including duppies, Maas Melville said.

By the time the cock crowed, it was only Maas Melville, Maas Jake, Justin, Nancy and me still awake. Gradually, everybody stirred and made their way out to climb up or down the hill, home, after a long night of story-telling.

12
Obeah

Hypocrites and parasites

Obeah is some people's religion. Even some of those hypocrites you see going to church; all sitting down inna front-row right under the parson's nose-hole, while they are still in the obeah business. Dem-deh kind of people! Their hands are as dirty as their hearts, for they know what they're doing isn't right. And some of them are bare-faced, you know, coming up to greet you with a brotherly kiss while at the same time they have kacoma working against you. Plenty people suffer through obeah and plenty people gain, but Massa Gaad naa sleep and the sum total of things, seen and unseen, will be un-veiled with time. Whenever you find people with a problem, you will find the obeah-man. Quite often, before certain people consider that what they are experiencing, bad as it is, might be something quite natural, they prefer to cry 'obeah' or else to go consult the obeah-worker for a solution. If a mosquito bites a woman's pickney and it gets malaria and dies, she gwine want to know who sent that mosquito to do that damage; more-be-less, she will be seeing obeah in the situation and, aggrieved, she might even seek out vengeance.

One particular obeah-man, Cuffee, was in our district, and the amount of people, sometimes from all over yonder, who used to find their way to his door is *more than John read 'bout*. But even if a whole heap of people weren't going to him, Cuffee wasn't the type of person to make business slacken off, for he always used to go create mischief. He had a way of going and telling this person that 'smady set someting fi dem' and how he could take it off if they paid him, or else he would set some bad omen inside your property and then come tell you how he got a 'revelation' about which part you should look to find the devilment. Sometimes people would find snake, bull-frog, black bat or some other creature or an evil-looking set-up or a bad smell in their property and have no idea how it could have reached there. This certain obeah-man, Cuffee, would convince plenty people that all manner of things would happen to them if they never eradicated the *guzu*. For a small price, he told them, he could break the curse. Nuff people would pay up good money to that *ginal*, but I never had time for any of his foolishness.

One time me ketch him in the yard, hiding behind some bushes near the house. I was certain he was planning to set something, for he had a bad reputation.

Me bawl out, 'Cuffee, yu dutty brute! Whe y'a do yah?'

Hear him, 'Lawd, yu frighten me.'

He was so shocked to see me, for he never expected anybody to see him crouching down in the bushes planning his wickedness. That man was sly and wily no fox.

I ran him off the place and told him how I would handle him if I ever found him up there again. But another time he came back up a yard and set something in the fire-hearth in the kitchen. We never knew anything about it, till Cuffee took sick some time later. As it happened, his daughter, Pearl, was looking after him and he told her he had to go out. Now, she wouldn't let him go anywhere because she knew he wasn't well enough to travel at all, but he insisted, so she asked him which part he had to go. He told her he had to go 'up a' Miss Emmie yard go tek out someting from inside har fire-heart.' Pearl told him she wouldn't let him go alone, so the two of them came up to my house that evening. Sure enough, the same place he set the thing; one ugly bundle of hocus-pocus, it was the same place he took it out. Pearl related to me everything he had told her. Him conscience mussi did a bother him mek Cuffee come tek out what him did set.

All the same, even if he never had come to take it out, I am certain that nothing untoward would have happened, because I always used to sweep out my fire-hearth before using it, and most times my *head would grow*, or I might smell something funny or my mind would warn me when something around the place wasn't right, so sooner or later I was bound to find that old bundle which Cuffee had set.

That Cuffee was a wicked man who used to prey on people's weakness, even tell them how he could help them achieve their ambition in life, or else tell people how he could deal with their enemies without raising a finger. All the while, fattening his pocket. He was a ginal, alright, but he also used to carry out acts of real wickedness too, real occult business, all to fill him belly.

He used to threaten his wife, Lucy, that if she wasn't his wife, he would 'show her someting!' How he hated that woman, but he couldn't do without her for he was illiterate, and she always used to read for him, cook his food, wash his clothes; everything. But plenty times he used to warn her that he was going to kill her. People had it going round that it was him same one who did kill his own mother, so nobody did undermine that threat.

The place where he lived was in a little house, tucked out of the way, off from where everybody else did live. All manner of strange things were in that yard; dead animals and human skulls, teeth, bones, many kinds of bushes, fossils, feathers, birds' nests, shells, sand, hair, incense and all variety of oils and potions, snake oil, even jars of blood. The obeah-man used to always walk about collecting all the ornaments he needed to do his 'wuk'; grave dirt, spirits from burial ground, bull-frogs, snakes, rats, bats, sea creatures, all kinds of things. Now, the tradition goes that when obeah-man is out and about on his business, he shouldn't stop or interrupt his mission, look back or talk to anybody. He should mek-haste do what him a-do, so on certain occasions, the obeah-men we knew about the place would pass and not greet anybody or else they would come in very suspicious, hiding out or tippy-toeing around the area up to no good. At those times especially, we would know they were on assignment, so to speak. That is why whenever me would see Cuffee close to fi-we house hiding in the bush or looking like he was up to no good, me would always cuss him and run him off the place. Me and him wasn't wrenkers. I let him know plain that I knew what he was up to and run him like daag. He was one of the biggest cowards you would ever come across, and would run away like when yu lick after young puppy. Some people use to ask me if I wasn't afraid of him and even tell me that, 'when him dead me a go tired fi see him face.' Lamb of me mumma! Afraid? How could I let a man like that cut the fool with me?

Come night-time when they think nobody can see them, all kinds of ole neaga used to tek time trip-trip up to Cuffee's yard to go buy his obeah: women who wanted another woman to leave her man alone, people who thought bad luck was following them, those who had to go a court going to find out what they should do to win the case, those sitting examinations and wanting to guarantee a pass, even young gal wanting a man to love. Those people could go buy parchment, talisman, oil or ointment to rub on themselves or the person they desired or despised; 'love-oil', 'luck potion', 'oil-of-success', 'love-me-long' 'hindrance', 'turn-back', 'conqueror' and the rest. Sometimes the obeah-man would bathe people and take his opportunity to feel up or interfere with the women and tell them, 'fear not, is all part o' de remedy.' For how they held the obeah-man in high regard or were afraid of him or even because they were craven for what they wanted, they never felt ashamed to go through all that. Plenty of those obeah-men would take advantage and turn round tell the people that Gaad tell them to do it that way.

Most people wouldn't know what the obeah-man was giving them, but nevertheless they were quick to take it, because they believed their fortune would change for the better. The kind of bush the obeah-man would bwoil up and give them could have even been poisonous, how dem fi know? Still, they were quick to put it to dem head and drink. If the person then took sick or anything happened to them, the obeah-man could say that the 'obeah' that was on them was too strong or that the affected person left it too late to come for the remedy by which time the condition had gone too bad to be removed – all kinds of excuses. The more bare-faced would tell their clients that they never had enough faith, for it is by faith alone that all things are possible.

Cuffee would mek plenty money giving read-up – telling people what evil had been set for them and offering to remove it, or predicting what the future held for such a one. One thing that logie man used to do was to travel to bury a vial in some rich people's yard. At night time, he would hide out and throw ice on their roof-top. The next day, when they come out to inspect, they wouldn't see not a single rock-stone so they would start think they were haunted and that duppy was tormenting them. The obeah-man now would do that for a couple of nights, then go and knock at the people's door and tell them that he had been sent 'a vision' that they had an enemy who had buried something evil in their yard. After agreeing a price, he would act like he was sensing something supernatural, even 'go inna spirit', working his way over to where he had buried the vial, and dig it up. They would be most amazed and relieved, whilst he would coolly instruct them to burn it. Simple as it sounds, it wasn't one and two he hooked that way.

All the same, the obeah-man, or 'science man', knew plenty about bush medicine and oftentimes there would be no mystery in what he gave the people, for they themselves could have bwoiled those bushes and roots at their own yard. From you're ignorant or simple-minded, there is no shortage of people in a this world ready to take advantage of you.

Cuffee wasn't a young man, and one year I remember how he just took sick. But more than that for he started to lose his mind same time. Me no know if somebody did interfere with his obeah materials, causing him to lose his power, or whether, as talk had it, he read too much of the Black Art Book; parts he should never have read, and that made him go insane. Anyway, from he became sick, day in and day out, he would sit down on his veranda and confess. Whenever yu hear wicked people a-confess, yu know seh a-dead dem a-go dead. They have to make sure to confess all the evil acts they have performed so that they can make peace with Gaad before they die and have to face the judgement, and the certainty of hell fire.

So, Cuffee was out a' veranda, undergoing a peculiar form of penance for all to see. Sometimes, he would send and call certain people to come and see him and when they did, he would tell them what and what he had done to them and ask forgiveness and on occasions he would instruct them what to do to put a matter to rights. For some people, it was quite a shock, for they would never have believed how the devil had interfered with them, so to speak.

Cuffee's wife, Lucy, would cook his meals, which had to be without salt, and she had to hand him his food from behind her back, that is, she wasn't allowed to face him to give him anything; she had to hand it backwards. She gave him a spoon to eat with and he took it from her and dashed it away. He decided to use his hands to eat with and as he ate one handful, he gave one handful to his duppy companions. This time you couldn't see anybody sitting down beside him, but all the while he would be eating and talking to his duppy hosts; his only friends, so close, they even shared his meals and had him call them by name. Once or twice, me and a friend would stand up from out a' wall and watch the carry on. It was like a tragic stage-show. We would shake our heads and watch the mad-man, for by now everyone acknowledged that he had really lost all reason;

whoever was brazen or fool-hardy enough, would burst out laughing for him to hear, but mostly folks would drift by with a quickened step, observe his antics and vanish. When he finished eating and feeding his duppy combolos, he would fling away the plate, him never business which part it land. Then he would sit down little more talking to himself and to the duppies, and confessing. Always confessing. Whenever he broke off his penance, it was to pick himself up and go inside to use the chamber pot, but when people came to look for him, he would haul out the stinking container full of shit and tell them, 'go nyam dat'. Mad as hell. When Cuffee eventually died, that was when certain kufenge became afraid, for some of them felt it was then that the obeah-man would be most powerful, and without any control. Certain folks locked their doors from early evening and didn't want to go out, even those people who were wrapped up in league with Cuffee would brace themselves to find out what kind of hell was going to break loose, and who would inherit the mantle and become his successor. They would even be cautious not to call Cuffee by name or go which part he used to walk, through fear. All the same, it was quite something when a character like that passed away in the district, for he did have so much influence over certain people's lives. Nuff of them must have wondered how they were going to make it now their doctor and high-priest was gone. But, we know plain that the same Gaad Almighty who gives life and takes it away, is the one to consult with our problems, for him caan' dead.

Black joint stick

One time two sisters had a furious fight and from that, they stopped talking to one-another. The younger one, Viola, decided to wuk all forms of obeah against her own sibling, Elsie. She took her time go see the obeah-man and told a whole heap of lies about what her sister had done. The obeah-man performed what he considered appropriate and took his payment. In no time at all, a whole heap of black bats just started showing up in the sister's yard. As soon as night fell, you would see the bats flying into the kitchen, inside the house, even into the latrine. As Elsie killed them and threw the creatures away, the same black bats would come back inside her place to harass her. How could you explain that? It was nothing more than black magic. Viola was trying to turn her sister mad or to otherwise destroy her through obeah. Elsie went and got some advice from a *myal-man* who told her to use a black joint stick to beat off the bats. Black joint was a kind of bush that just grows about the place, and the limbs are very strong. After she used that to beat off the bats and kill them, she started a fire to burn the remains, but lo and behold, when you looked, there was not a drop of ashes to be seen.

Daag Foot

There was a woman living in our district, Muriel, whom everybody did call, 'Daag Foot'. They called her so because she used to run up and down with a married man and when his wife, Mable, got to find out, she paid a visit to her obeah-man and then went to confront the man's lover. Mable bawled her out on the road one day in a heavy temper, 'Why yu won't leave me husban'? I gwine give yu someting fi mek yu stop it. After all him don't belong to yu.'

After she said that, she took a broom from behind her back and started to beat her rival on her foot. Within a couple days after that, the woman's foot broke out in all manner of sores, all over, like when yu see dutty maaga daag with all manner of nasty open sores all over their body, and the stinking smell that was its companion.

From then, the name 'Daag Foot' just set on her; that was what they called her, though not to her face. All the same, yu had to feel sorry for the woman, although she was a *licky-licky*, nyamy-nyamy kind of person who used to have her hands in anything that was not good. She always used to walk up and down begging money to borrow, but she did practice obeah so plenty people never wanted to lend her in case she took their money and used it to obeah them.

Once, one of our neighbours, my good friend, Hermione, had quite a disturbing experience with Miss Daag Foot. Hermione had a young son named Wesley, who decided to raise rabbits. He had a couple of them which he planned to breed, so he built a cage for them, made preparations for adequate feeding and was going on fine as ever. Now, Daag Foot did have a son named Pauley who took it upon himself to come and tief one of Wesley's rabbits. All upon a sudden he had rabbits and he never had any before. Wesley, realising what had gone on, went up to their yard and told them he wanted his rabbit back, but they told him it wasn't his. When he saw that they had decided not to give it back, Wesley killed the rabbit. He must have reasoned that since him naa get it, them shouldn't have it either.

As he pulled out his pen-knife and slit the rabbit's throat, Daag Foot got vexed and cried out, 'Yu missa Wesley, the same foot yu tek walk up yah, yu gwine want it an' caan' get it fi use.'

Now, I got to understand that when a wicked person blows you a warning like that, it is not something to take lightly. If they say, 'eye' then you should watch your hand, if they say mouth, then you should watch your foot. In other words, you should take anything they say seriously, for they won't rest until they have committed some act of wickedness in retribution against you.

The next day, as God is my witness, the bwoy Wesley got up and started hopping like a rabbit. His feet started swelling and he couldn't walk properly at all. They called a doctor who gave the bwoy an injection, but it was no good. As the days went by, his condition only got worse, till smady told his mother, Hermione, to carry the lad to see a certain woman called Auntie Dolly clear over Manchester. By this, the bwoy was jumping like a rabbit for real; all he could do was hop.

When dem go a Manchester to Auntie Dolly's place, which, truth be told, came in like a balmyard, they made Wesley and his mother recite something from the Bible and then asked them if they believed the Lawd could heal him, to which they answered, 'yes'. Auntie Dolly made him tu'n-him-roll and prayed over his foot. When she finished, the young man and his mother walked home as good as ever; no more jumping like a rabbit, and they never even had to pay any money.

When they reached back home and Daag Foot saw that the obeah had been taken off, she was surprised but what she could-a do?

Some time later, they have revival meeting in the district and a parson from the Salvation Army came up especially to preach. The meeting hall was packed out, and everybody was waiting for Holy Ghost power to manifest. They started taking up testimonies about what the Lawd had done in the lives of the 'saints' in that gathering, and Daag Foot stood up to share her testimony, but somebody called out, 'Yu a get up fi testify an' yu same one wuk obeah 'pon a young man to give him rabbit foot, a dat yu a go testify 'bout?'

Some people burst out laughing and some cried, 'shame', until the meeting got out of hand and they ran Daag Foot from the place in disgrace. They never allowed that woman to forget the evil she did over that young man's rabbit. Just like how she would never forget how a married woman did obeah her for committing adultery with her husband. The brand was there, on her two foot, for all to see. Even when Daag Foot did go to get baptised, some years later, she made sure to keep on her water boots so people wouldn't notice how she was covered with all manner of *yaws*.

Good and evil

Many people don't know the power there is in this world; power for good and power for evil.

For every poison, there is an antidote, and for every problem, there is a solution. Oftentimes the innocent really suffer because they lack the knowledge to know how to deal with wickedness. Yu could be going on about your business, fine and dandy, when all upon a sudden, affliction strikes. When you tek a stock, you find out that it is somebody who doesn't like you who has done something to put your life in misery. Not all the time, but back in the old days, we did have a real sense of obeah because evil-minded people were working it all the time; it came in like they never slept. We would get to learn about what was no good, what was a deliberate set up and what the power of Gaad could do to help you overcome. Whenever you talk about obeah, people look at you like your head a gather water, but I know what I'm talking about. Wickedness didn't just start today.

Arlene was a pickney gal in the district who was bright so till. She won all manner of prizes in school and to all intents an' purposes, she was the one all the teachers, headmaster and even her classmates were certain would be successful in life. But not everybody did love that. Me dear mah! Yu know what happened? They set that child to go blind. One morning she left her yard, as fit as ever, but when she came back home from school that evening, she was as blind as a bat. She was walking and tumbling over; couldn't see at all where she was going. Lawd Jesus! They had to lead her to go in the house, out to the latrine, any where she had to go. The poor pickney took it to heart so much, all she would do was to sit under the pimento tree and pine. She was just so pitiful pondering whether that was how she would spend the rest of her life. After all, she was only about thirteen. Now, her people got to understand that it was somebody who 'set' her so, all because she bright. Her family carried her to a madda-woman with a good reputation for healing through Bible reading and a fervent belief in Father, Son and Holy Ghost. They asked the child simply if she believed and she answered that she did. A mighty puff of smoke came down before the gathering and the Holy People touched her eyes and prayed that they be opened, like the tomb of Lazarus. Little after that, the child could see as good as before, nobody needed to lead her anywhere again. She was still bright, but after that she she never could live up to the promise of before. Before too long, her people moved from the district to try and start over afresh. It always amazes me how people can be surprised or unbelieving whenever we talk about obeah, especially in a world like this where wicked people don't sleep until they have mashed up somebody's life; how can I see all I have seen, and not acknowledge that obeah is a powerful force? If you wear a good dress, there's bound to be someone who will covet you. If you do good, they covet you. If people like you and are always blessing you, there will be someone else who will covet that, and beyond all that, they will use obeah to try and destroy your progress. But, you know, anyhow you don't understand the nature of evil, how it is all around, and try to find out how Gaad can help you, you won't stand at all for they will crush your very life.

Poco

My mind just run on those Poco people who used to hold their meetings clear over yonder bush. They dressed up all in white; even down to their drawers and slip had to be white, the women's heads had to be covered, and all with feet bare. We used to stay clear up a-yard and hear the 'a-humma, a-humma' trooping going on. Their leader, the Shepherd, had a crook in one hand and a notorious bull-whip in the other, and with those two objects, that man ruled his congregation with the iron discipline of a sergeant major. If you ever wanted to hear all manner of unknown tongues, or see people 'get inna spirit', Poco meeting was the place to go. Me no know what kind of spirit, oh, but some would fall into a trance and carry on wild while the duppy did just a-ride them. Those spirits, duppies, would enter those people and carry them go even up inna coconut tree and bring them down backway.

Poco a no easy something. One time, Custus Johnson marched into a Poco meeting to go drag out his wife, Mimi, after he done warn her plenty times not to go there. As he set off from the house, people in the meeting later reported how Shepherd blew a warning telling them, 'enemy a come', and they started to jump and 'a-humma', all the more. As Custus entered the place, the Shepherd palmed the whip and beat that man, running him out of the meeting hall and in his haste to escape, Custas ran into some barbed wire which hooked him till Shepherd finished with him. Needless to say, Custas was never again so bold and left his wife to her religion.

Another time, Miss Gertel's sister, Gladys, did have a stroke over in America where she was living. Quick o'clock, she came up to look for Gertel to see if her minister could lift the 'blow', for she was certain it wasn't any natural medical condition that had brought her low, but none other than obeah. Miss Gertel dutifully carried Gladys to a Poco meeting, and as they sat down in the service, Shepherd quickly jumped up crying, 'a word of knowledge, of knowledge, of knowledge a-come fi a visitor fram a far-off shore.' Well, Gertel got excited and so did Gladys but that was nothing to the excitement of the congregation, for the amount of shouting, jumping and unknown tongues that broke out in there. As Shepherd repeated again about 'word of knowledge', one of the congregation went into a heavy wailing, shaking and what's it, so till Shepherd's message got interrupted and he couldn't deliver it again. Everytime the message was to come, it got delayed, interrupted or interfered with, three times that same thing happened and three times Gladys had to pay for the lifting of the same 'blow' till her time and money ran out and she had to go back to America paralysed same way.

13
Hard Times

> Annotto can't sell, the price is unfair
> pimento a-blossom and drop
> hard time a carry the day
> for they won't put cramouchin away

War

We had a feeling war was going to break out sooner or later, same as how you'd know when a hurricane was going to strike. The years before the official announcement of war were lean, hard years; hard times. There was food scarcity, strikes all over, even down at Frome the workers did up-rise on one of the sugar estates, and it kind of ignited other areas too, like in a chain. In little and no time at all, we were hearing about workers clashing with police, some people even getting killed, and canefields being set a-fire. It wasn't Frome alone such things were happening, it was all over; a kind of under-daag up-rising was manifesting. On top of that, war came in to compound the feeling of chaos and confusion. It wasn't a thing to say that what was going on overseas was of no concern to us in little Jamaica, for from you see Germany had troubled England, it came in like they had offended one of our closest friends. Those bad bwoys around the place used to have a saying, 'touch one a we, yu haffi touch all a we'. It was the same with the war. Little after Germany bruised up Poland and France, they decided to take on England, put the Englishman's nose out of joint with all that blitzing, then Hitler took it upon himself to go provoke America, so you must know that our people were rightfully vexed about the situation; from England had hostilities with Germany, then Jamaica had to be in it to defend the Empire. Only one drawback. Our people get so excited about these things, you would think it was Montego Bay or out at Negril the Germans were ready to invade the way some people were carrying on. The war talk and accounts of daring-do was such that you would scarcely believe the action was taking place a-foreign, not on our little island. Who wasn't giving advice about what had to be done to 'Hitla' was advocating the war plan about how 'Missa Chu'chill' should order the war.

It was hard to imagine what was really going on, the full scope of everything, since our outlook was so limited, and, after all, who mattered our opinion? In fi-we tiny area, we never even knew much about carbine and gun-powder, much less about artillery and infantry and all, but we read about the war in the *Gleaner* newspaper and passed on what we read, sometimes touching it up here and there, in the same way you might add little seasoning to food to make it more palatable. It made us swell-headed to know that some of our own soldiers were going a-foreign to fight shoulder to shoulder with the British and American forces; some were in RAF, others in Marines. But never mind war strategy, what mainly affected us during those blighted years, was everyday living; how to eat and keep everything we had together when so much rationing and shortage was in operation. You couldn't get sugar to buy unless you did buy soap, or flour unless you did buy shaving cream, or sewing thread. Or, come to that, oil unless yu did buy hair pomade. As to rice and milk – forget it – it come in like they did migrate. Shopkeepers had decided to 'marry' the goods; those products that were in high demand would get married off with something they couldn't shift. It was a sly kind of a way to make a profit and that's the way they used to shock it. Those store-owners had a way of mixing white rice with brown – that is when rice put in an appearance at all. The two strains come in like brown pickney and white pickney already; you notice the difference, but when it is cooking, it feava the two types of rice was in an argument; for brown rice is very 'loud' you can stay clear over yonder and smell it cooking and it takes longer, while white rice is more delicate and gives no trouble at all.

Many nights were spent in darkness because of the oil shortage; not a drop to dress the lamps, and if you had candles you were doing well. If you were good friends with the shop-keeper then he would make sure to take care of you. When a consignment of Betty milk came in, you, who name ordinary Jack and Jill, naa get none, but his friends would get plenty. The rest would get put down while everyday the price would hike right up. The war gave those store-owners a chance to reign as king and over-lord for a time, although even at the best of times, they did always used to milk people good and proper. It seemed the war gave them more excuses to do that. And you know, it is just the way of the world that it is when you can't get a thing that you really miss it, so the price controls and rationing really set your mind on trying to acquire something you had a hankering for. Otherwise you just had to do your utmost to try and replace it with something close. You know, like you would have a hankering for salt-fish, but that was off, so you tried to make your own salt-ting although that was a problem in itself because you couldn't get salt and fresh fish was a rarity.

Country people were used to managing hardships all the time, but during the war we had to come up more ingenious. A man might sell a pig for a premium price and then buy a bag of flour and make a good profit off that; sell some, use some a-yard and even barter with some.

Also, during war-time, you tried your utmost to hang on to whatever money you had rather than spending it. Everybody was out to pinch from you so you had to be more penny-pinching in return, for you never knew if things were due to pick up or get *wus*. You can already imagine how meat-kind was scarce down to fresh fish, although to me that never made sense for we were still living close to the sea same as before. Still, it looked like most of everything ended up in town and especially wherever the military people stationed themselves. Otherwise, it is truly hard to explain how come there was so much shortage. Still, we who were always used to hard times just use to press on through. We had the land, and were not going to starve. More besides, we realised from day one that *every mickle mek a muckle* so survival was never a problem. When soap shortage did lick, even brown soap and blue-soap were hard to come by. Some people would rush the shops like harbour sharks and buy up the produce and stock them up in their yard so things would often run out quick a shop, and that way the price would get pushed right up through the roof. To wash clothes when there was no soap, some people used to use the ackee skin and carry the clothes to the river-side to wash, beating those garments against flat rocks to get out all the dirt. There was always a way to manage. You could still make your own starch from cassava and anyhow you could get 'blue' that would whiten the garments perfectly well, otherwise, the sun would bleach them well enough.

One of the scarcest things around was work. Daag an' all did a look wuk, down to wuk did a look wuk! Some of the young people in the area tried to get jobs with overseas service or else tried for employment in town with a military station, although to tell the truth most of them would've settled for any kind of labour whatsoever, from domestic to watch-man, although the young women had another motive; to get close to yankee soldiers. There were plenty enough idiots in the rum-bars, like Percival Grant, who used to talk big about wanting to go a Germany 'go bomb Hitla'. That rum talk was well strong, but ask that same man to do the smallest thing and you would see how quickly he could vanish like six o'clock fog. The way money was scarce came in like it was on a permanent vacation, and sometimes even hope appeared to be in short supply.

It was hard times alright, but who had sense learned to button their lip and not to bother talking about what they had or what they were planning to do so that idle people could begrudge them and hinder their plans. We up-a-yard just used to keep our heads down and, as the saying goes, work out our own salvation. All the same, we used to wonder what would happen when the war was over and shop-keepers couldn't form the fool pricing up the goods like it was the crown jewels they were selling. Nuff people did have long memories and couldn't wait to trace the store-keepers about their thiefing ways all throughout the hardship of the war.

Hurricane

June too soon,
July, stand by!
August, come it must!
September, remember!
October, all over!

Hurricane would never just strike so, it always followed warnings, so people had time to prepare.

It was amazing to know that the animals and birds, down to the smallest ant, would know hurricane a come. Massa Gaad is so merciful he always gives his creatures time to prepare for the worst of calamity. The 1948 hurricane was one I will always remember, coming in on the tail-end of the war with a vexatious madness. The warning had gone out, so anybody a-yard who were preparing to travel would know to postpone their trip, and all hands would be needed to help secure the house, for hurricane is no picnic. When you see the wind go fi blow, all some trees that got bowed or were up-rooted, zinc roof fly off-a house or buildings that got washed away, and all the while the lashing of the rain and beating, noisy, driving wind, howling like a giant in terminal pain, while the wind lashed those shutters and the lightning caused our hearts to leap.

Me dear, mah! This time all of us were locked up in that house for five good days, the pickney dem set up play-house under the bed, and using whatever area they could find again to play jacks, marble, mumma–puppa or doctor and nurse. The animals dem would be penned in securely, some under-house or some even in the yard or in the kitchen. Day and night that wind would blow. Sometimes thunder would clap, lightning flash, and we prayed to Massa Gaad, and read Psalm 91, for it is not a word of a lie to say some of us really believed the world was going to end. There used to be a song which says there would be no hiding place on the Last Day, 'Yu run to the rock, the rock caan' hide yu, for the rock want a hiding place for itself.' A better call to prayer for the doubtful than lightning and thunder and the threat of brimstone and fire, I cannot imagine. We would have to run out a-kitchen to prepare food, and by the time you were to run back inside, if you never mind sharp, rain-water would catch inside the vessels and spoil everything. Umbrellas hardly had any use in those conditions, for the wind would drag it and bend it like a child with a latch-pin. The amount of umbrellas and roof-tops we would see up in trees months after a hurricane was over, placed there like trophies and a reminder that the monster breeze did pass through.

During the '48 storm, a woman named Ruby Calder gave birth to a little pickney bwoy and they christened him Rufus, after him pa. Within three months, that child had cut his first teeth and was uttering his first words. True. Some people took that as a sign that he was going to be a prophet and gave him a pet-name, Elijah. Meanwhile, some beheld it as sinister, and declared that from that happened and with how he had been delivered during hurricane time, it was a bad sign. The muttering started to go round that the pickney wouldn't live, others had it that he would grow up to turn obeah-man. But Ruby never bothered to cuss and carry on, she just gave Gaad thanks for 'the blessing he had chosen to bestow 'pon him hand-maiden'. For a while she did carry on a little pious and holy-holy; everything was 'blessed' this and 'blessed' that, so that some people started calling her Virgin Mary, but she never mattered a soul till long after the season lifted.

There was a fearless fellow around the place going by the name of Lightning Jack who came with a marvellous history, for twice in his life during hurricanes, lightning struck him and he lived. Folks expected that after the first time he wouldn't be too righted, much less live to tell the tale, let alone for it to happen twice, yet Jack was a miracle, walking. During hurricane time, the one thing I never stopped marvelling over, is how, with the amount of trees that got up-rooted and houses that tumbled-down or got washed away, how it was that the old houses, built from way back when, which always looked like they couldn't withstand any amount of pressure, would stand firm and unmoved when time hurricane was done, while, blam!, the newer houses would just flatten like how you would-a mash ants nest. That is a thing I will always ponder over.

Hard time preacher

Whenever hard times occurred, you would always find certain preachers that travelled up and down the place giving *prophecy fi breadfruit*. Plenty people would lose their property to those bogus preachers on the prowl like devouring lions. They would go from district to district cleaning out all the few meagre possessions that people had, and tainting the name of religion. Most times it would be a *samfie man* going around the place masquerading as a preacher, with a band of light-fingered 'converts', who were as quick to give a testimony as they were to rob you blind. One time, a group of them came up to Mountain and some weak-hearted simpletons ran with open arms to welcome them.

The 'preacher' had his American Bible tracts and neck collar, and everything he said began or ended with, 'tanks be to Gaaa-ad', in a yankee twang, or with, 'holding fas' to Gaaa-ad's unchanging hand', and many other such sayings as he beat on his his big, black King James Bible. The way he held on when he called the name of God, 'Gaaaa-ad', (like him did a yawn), made many believe that just as how he held on to the name and wouldn't let it go, the same way he was holding on to the Almighty on his god-sent mission to our humble little area. So, the following day, they kept a prayer meeting, and a certain fellow called Honeywell who, some said, came from over Lamb's Town, jumped up off his chair and shouted out, 'Hallelujah, tenk Gaad me can walk!' He dashed away the walking stick and everybody marvelled at how that cripple could walk. The 'preacher' even made him run from one end of the meeting hall to the other, whooping, 'glory!' as he ran. From that, people ran go carry their offering to the man of God because they wanted a miracle too. One, Lancelot Blackwood, carried his sow go give them after they did 'prophesy' and tell him how he was going to be a rich man. The preacher told him, 'Thus says the Lawd, give and it shall be given unto thee good measure pressed down, shaken together and running over. So sayeth the word-a Gaaaa-ad to you, man.' Old man Blackwood, who had a wicked stammer, tied up his pig to carry go give them, and when the wife disagreed, he told her he wouldn't want her again for he was going to get a blessing and since she was double-minded like Lot's wife, who, he reminded her, 'became a pillar of s-s-s-salt', she wouldn't get even 'de dust from off a shilling' out of it. The only thing he never did to that poor woman was to call her 'Doubting Thomas'. By the time he finished berating her, it was easy to imagine that him as wealthy as he was unwise.

Plenty others who never took livestock carried a shilling, sixpence or whatever little money they had go give the 'prophet'. Him did really profit fi true! Some even started rolling and chatting in 'unknown tongues'. One woman, Eunie Gray, got a message from the 'preacher' that he saw a '*pan-a-jar*' coming up right before her and said he would reveal where she was to start digging. The next day she carried her cow go give that man. It wasn't till after those rogues had departed in the dead of night, that she and the others found out they had been deceived.

Hear Lancelot, 'Lawd, me one sow!' From that, the name just fixed on as people called him, 'One-Sow'. Another one they named, 'Bogle-Bogle' for how he had been 'speaking in tongues', and the one who was looking untold riches, Miss Eunie, they nicknamed, 'Pan-a-Jerry-de-cow-gaan'. In hard times, apart from shop-keepers, it was only 'Preach-an'-Gaan' samfie-man who used to get rich quick.

Kendal crash

One of the most terrible tragedies I can remember was the Kendal crash. I did know of two people who took that fateful train journey on their way to church outing going from Kingston to Montego Bay, but, lawd, what mishaps caused the train to turn over causing so many to lose dem life is a mystery. Margie Taylor, my childhood chum, was going on the trip that day but because of sickness she never did go and we rejoiced for that but truly I mourned for all who did lose dem life and all who lost loved ones. Whether it is story or not, me no certain, but talk have it that the passengers did a misbehave 'pon de train causing commotion and distressing all the nuns. Me no know what happened when it reach Kendal for it to run off the line. The whole nation mourned over that disaster and some even questioned how Gaad could let such a thing happen to church people. We may wonder and ponder such matters but in this world there are more questions than answers. One thing, the amount o' duppy story whe' emerge from Kendal crash is nobody's business. Countless taxi-drivers gave account of how they ferried passengers to a particular address and waited outside while the passenger went inside to get the payment. After a time the driver would knock on the door and would describe his passenger only to be told, 'That sound like my daughter but she did dead inna Kendal crash.'

Sewing machine

I did own a sewing machine, one of the hand-turning types. After saving up for more months than I have fingers to count, that beautiful machine which I saw over at a hardware store in Montego Bay, was mine. Every so often I would go pay down towards it, and although the shop manager came to trust me and offered to give me the machine to use until I finished paying for it all, I told him I would pay first. Well, at last the time came and no-one was more gleeful than me when it was finally mine. Believe me, it was quite something to be able to sew all me *batrawn* on a machine rather than doing it all by hand as before. I don't rightly remember how much it did cost but it took many trips to Newmarket, Belmont and Whitehouse with the heap of produce atop me head to go sell before I could afford it. We were fascinated when we first learned that there was such a thing as sewing machine, for it was truly marvellous and labour-saving. What I never used it to sew doesn't bear mentioning. I made handkerchiefs, drawers, pants, shirts, frocks, school uniform, you name it. One of the first articles I sewed on that machine was a white cotton 'kerchief for my third boy, Linval. He used to say that when he took it out of his pocket and wiped his face, he loved it all the better. He must still have it to this day.

One day I was up a-yard sewing when I had a visit from a travelling tradesman named Lewis. Now, unbeknown to me at the time, that was not his rightful name, for he was moving up and down all over the country and everywhere he went, he used a different name. That ginal. Anyway, this particular day, Lewis called on me and said it was always good to look over a machine, even if it looked to be working as good as ever, because at certain times they were all good to break down and the parts were hard to come by. He sounded so charming and knowledgeable that I was really taken in. After all, I never knew anything about such matters and what if it was to break down on me? So, Lewis came into the house, inspected the sewing machine and informed me that a part was missing. He told me that, as it so happened, he had the right part and how much it would cost to fix the machine.

Just then Linval came in through the back door. That took Lewis by surprise, for he never knew that that any body was at home with me. Linval told him to hand over the machine part that he removed.

Lewis replied, 'Ah don't know what yu talking about fella, me no have nothin' inna me pocket'. But as Linval went to approach him the man got jumpy and rushed out the door. As he was running down the steps he was somehow wrong-footed and dropped to the ground, blap! He must have mashed his face real hard because him nose did a bleed. He got up and started acting like *Mary McCloud* was in his underpants, rushing out the gate and hollering blue murder and bawling out so loud everybody came running; even those out in the fields dropped their tools, those in their house put down whatever they were doing and came to see what was going on. They must have believed that somebody was truly getting murdered. When they came, they beheld the man with the blood 'pon him face causing a commotion and pointing to me – me him point to – claiming it was me who lick him and me who was going to kill him. lmagine!

They called Pilate, the District Constable, and when the policeman came, Lewis told him how me rushed after him with a machete and was threatening to kill him. He started to bewail and who wouldn't take pity for how he looked like a hurt puppy. True to his name as a wicked overseer of Bible days, Pilate hauled me go a-station. The people all cried 'shame', and urged him to let me go, but the DC was quite determined though he never put the *bangle* on me and I simply went along with him and didn't utter a word even when he took me to the station and they put me in the lock-up overnight. *Me dear mah! From me baan come a worl' me never imagine such a ting would befall.*

First thing the next morning, my people came to bail me and the police gave me a paper to sign and told me that I would get a summons to attend court. When the time came, I got the order to go to court – up the four-an-twenty steps – as we called it. In those days it was quite a disgrace for you to have to go a-court any-at-all but I never felt ashamed for I knew I was innocent. Plenty people came to offer support.

Hear a woman named Dovey, 'Jesus Gad, Miss Emmie, no fret. Me know yu no guilty, even blind man can see dat yu never do it.' In the court-room, my case got called and the judge said I was there for carrying out damage to Lewis. Him asked me how me plead. I said, 'not guilty, sah'.

Lewis stood up and told a whole heap of lies about how me

threaten to murder him. I couldn't contain my peace so I shouted out, 'No tell no lie 'pon me.' This time the court-house was full up of people with grievances against Lewis, for he did go round and do the same thing up and down the place beguiling people. From word got out that he was to appear in court, people reached there in the hope that they could get justice. Some stood up and bear witness that Lewis was a criminal and even called him by the crooked name him did give them at the time; some had 'Missa Smiley', some 'Jacob Miller', another one, 'John Milton'. And plenty others got up and demanded back money him did swindle from them. Hear them, 'Yu brute yu! Yu love tell lie but yu gwine haffi stop now.'

The judge called order in the court and pronounced me 'not guilty'. Lewis dashed out of the court-house so fast with the court marshal and all rushing after him. We walked home that evening. It wasn't one or two miles from the court-house but as we were going along, the big full moon just came up and spread out itself like a valance almost as the sun was fully setting but it came in like broad day-light for the brightness of that moonlight. As we were going along, all the neighbours who saw us on the road came up and said they were certain we would win.

After that, anywhere I saw the Lewis bwoy, I let him know I was going to give him a good licking so whenever he saw me, he would always run. After a time word got round that him was in prison for larceny. As for Pilate, after the court-case I never said a word to him. Me meet it already with evil-minded people, but all me know is, 'who Gaad bless no man curse'.

Pilate

It was me who decided to call that wicked *kaap*i 'Pilate', because of how he operated; cruel as a bluebeard. From that man went and joined police, he started walking around the place like him one have all the power under Gaad's heaven and anytime he had a grudge against anybody, they had better watch out, for he was a spiteful, vindictive character. Not all of them, but plenty police officers did have a reputation for bribery and such like, and could always be relied upon to rough up people they never liked. One time, Pilate lined up the police down at his head-quarters to go up a' Anson Hill under the pretext that the people up there were growing ganja and smoking the weed tough-tough. I got to understand that Pilate even tek time go give some of his police chums down a-station some ganja for their own use and told them, 'No mek dem know seh a me give yu.' Yet he still set them up to come search up at Anson Hill, a little way off from our place. Whenever police came to carry out such assaults, often looking for fugitives, not a warning would sound, only they never came to raid a' night-time because up in the hills it was so dark and full up o' bush that anybody they were looking for was bound to get away or hide out carefully, especially like how they knew the area better than the police. So, usually, whenever the police raided, they came very early in the morning. And, mek me tell you, dem naa come so far out, all dung in some gully bush, fi fun. They always had a Judas, that is a police informer, who would give them the signal when to come and who they were to aim for. This particular time, it was Pilate who set up the whole thing so at break of day, a band of police rushed up to Anson Hill and started pounding on Miss Ethline's door. Now, she and her sister, Pinny, used to bwoil ganja-tea for sickness all the time.

One of the kaapis shouted out: 'Police, open up!'

Poor Miss Ethline, her sister Pinny and her son, Kwabena, were in the house, still in bed, and Miss Ethline flew out to find out what was going on. The police told her it was ganja they were looking for.

Hear Miss Ethline, 'Me no know what name so.'

At that the police pushed past her with all manner of unpleasant speech and forty-shilling bad-wud and started to search the house but they couldn't find any ganja bush inside or any growing out a-yard, only some in a bottle which Pinny told them she did brew for 'medicinal usage'. When they saw the son, Kwabena, they grabbed him and started to man-handle the lad. After all, it was him they did go up there for under Pilate's instructions: he was one of those 'back-to-Africa' people dem call Rasta. When they captured him they set him up by putting some ganja in the young man's pocket and claimed, 'A deh-so dem fin' it.'

Hear one of them, 'Wha' dat inna yu pocket?'

Kwabena answered, 'Nothin' no in deh.' But one of the officers reached in and just fished out the set-on.

The kaapi said, 'A wha' dis?'

The youth replied, 'Me no know, sar.'

They boxed him in his face and told him, 'yu too lie' and straight away they put on the bangle.

We now were roused by the commotion of daags barking, and came out in time to see the police marching the young fellow down to the station; two daags at his heels and held fast by handcuffs for all to see. He was begging them to let him go and pleading his innocence but hear one of the police, 'No tell me warrawarrahit.' Poor Ethline and Pinny did just a-bawl and the police run those women out the way, although plenty people did rally round to comfort them and tell them 'no mind'. By this, from it was clear police were in the area, all who did have ganja a-grow run out quick go pull it up. There was no time to burn it. You mad? That smell would lead police straight to you, so when they up-rooted the sensimelia, some went and threw away the crop down the latrine and some even tried to bury it or hide it good till after 'Babylon gaan'.

It did always come in funny how the police would set out so purposefully to find ganja since it is something that grows naturally all over the place. We country people use that herb, like many others, to bwoil for making tea and to use as medicine. Regulation came in to cut out ganja smoking and the ganja trade, and it looked like they never wanted the weed to grow any-at-all.

So, anyway, that morning, all who had ganja were in hiding, locked up inna dem yard or else went to hide out dung a-gully until after the police passed through the area.

They carried the youth up to police head-quarters and beat him black and blue. After that, they locked him up for two whole days. For what? It wasn't ganja, you know. Remember me did tell you how Pilate did have malice for the young man and then decided to spite him. He took to walking about the place and talking how he was going to teach the youth a lesson. It wasn't the first person he did that to, either. Ethline and the bwoy's aunt, Pinny, went to find a lawyer-man to represent Kwabena, and when the case went to court, the judge flung it out. He said, 'no case to answer', and he blew a warning to the police that they should be more careful in future. After that, anytime Pilate saw Ethline, he made sure he didn't trouble her. If she walked here, he walked deh-so for she did threaten 'fi bus' him *warra*'. That wily man did have a wife, Mary-gale, who they used to call, 'Waganess', on account of how she did walk and kind of waddle because of her arthritis. (From you get an affliction, Jamaica people christen you with a new name; it doesn't make sense to quarrel or frown, the most you can do is grin and bear it.) Now, Pilate used to drink rum like it was water and anytime he saw a woman he desired, he would just drag her go a him yard an' ting; have his way with her and no business who didn't like it, especially his wife. All she, you couldn't tell Mary-gale anything bad about her husband, for she wouldn't believe you. Dem was *batty an' bench*. It wasn't one or two times me had problems with that man. For whatever reason, he had a grudge against me and my family, but I told him plain not to try and set me or my people up for a thing.

Hear him, 'Who you, Auntie Emmie?' – he always called me 'Auntie'. I told him emphatically, 'Dis-yah same bitch yah!'

Thiefing kaapi

Pilate was good friends with another kaapi in the area, Manuel Jacobson, who everyone did call, 'Fagin'. He was the whip to the other policeman's lash. The reason they called him Fagin was he was a 'baan t'ief', who used to support his wife and pickney dem through thiefing goods; that is to say, he was a very light-fingered fellow; anything he saw, he took and he had a way of always going to the butcher and shop-keeper to 'trust' his goods, but he would always find a way not to pay for a bean or a button. He owed guinea here, guinea there, guinea every blooming where. The very house and land he lived in was not his own, his wife, Joycelyn, a tough, *mampy* woman, had been another man's before he took up with her and even the very uniform on his back was hand-me-down. He even used to tek him pickney dem out go t'ief with him. One night, he and his son, Kenny, got caught in smady's field stealing out their crops. The owner tek time hide and saw all what Father Puss and son were doing. As the bwoy went to pull up, of all things, a guinea co-co, the root burst.

Hear him to the father, 'Daadee, de co-co pop.'

The puppa said, 'Shut yu bloomin' mout'!'

The person who was watching it all could scarcely keep from laughing out loud, and afterwards had the whole episode going around the district and from that, they christened the father, 'Fagin Co-co' and baptised the son, 'Artful Dodger'. That little bwoy was rude and out of order, you see! One time he boxed my youngest gal-pickney, Elizabeth – Betty. Me seh Ma! The two of them were going to the same school, although he was a little older than she. Me no know what happened to make him decide to pick 'pon her, but the bwoy go box the chile and told her how 'her nose broad like when cow shit 'pon flat rock'. And the box him box her, me no know if her nose did bleed or what, but she was sorely distressed. When she reached home that afternoon, I asked her what happened and she told me. She could hardly get to set foot through the gate for I simply wheeled her roun' go up to where that little ruffian, Kenny, lived. When we reached, his mother, Hortense, greeted me, 'howdy-do', and asked me if anything was the matter. I greeted her and related how it was her bwoy me did come to see. I called him over to me and asked him if he did box Betty in her face.

He said 'Yes, mam.'

So I asked him if he did bruk her nose if he could-a fix it back.

He replied, 'No, mam.' Then I called Betty, who was lingering behind me frock-tail, and told her to box him back right inna him face, and she did it. After all, box fi box is no robbery.

His mother said, 'That's right', for she knew that if it wasn't a serious matter, I wouldn't have gone up to her yard any-at-all. You see, from that little bwoy started boxing gal pickney, he would box his wife when he turned a man, and that would never do; you have to bend the tree from it young.

Fagin, Kenny's pa, was never wicked like Pilate, but he was just as much a disgrace to his office as a policeman, for, not only did he used to be a thief – stealing did come in like his profession – but he used to cuss bad-wud and drink to a scandalous extent. When his friend Pilate took sick and died, it took a little time before they managed to tell the wife for she used to fret a whole heap, and for how she was devoted to that man, they must have been afraid of how she might have taken the news, and what she might have done to herself. Fagin, now, did go mad. Mad as shad. Shortly before he died, he locked himself up in his room with his chamber-pot while making confession, and plastered those four walls with his mess.

14
Belly Full but we Hungry

Ram goat liver

When celebration time came around any-at-all, we always used to butcher a goat. I have done even that myself already; after all a no nothin' to string up a goat and slaughter it, but, all the same, it was mostly the men who used to do it. Some women can be so soft and delicate like toilet soap; they hear the goat a-bawl, 'wheeah!' and they tek foot, run; yet they have nothing to say when the goat meat is curried and ready to eat. After you kill the goat, you skin it and singe the head over the open fire, scraping off all the hair. The skin has certain uses for whoever wants it to make a bag, a floor mat or a drum. The head would be put in a galley a-fire along with the goat seed, some *scotch bonnet*, *skellion*, thyme, bay-leaf, pimento leaf and some other herbs to boil up to make mannish water. That soup is really strengthening; I used to hear them with a song saying how, 'it mek yu daata walk an' talk'. The ram goat liver now, that was my lover. I always used to fry it up separately and eat with boiled green bananas, or else I would give it to one of the children who was looking anaemic to help build up their body. But most times, whenever I cooked that liver, vulgar as it sounds, I would take it and lick it, then suck it all over before biting into it and really enjoying myself. Some people bwoil it up in mannish water, but I loved ram goat liver fried up all to meself. Joy.

Curry goat

Curry goat was always something to enjoy. They prepared that to eat especially for a wedding, while the gerrey was going on; music playing, people dancing, and a heap of singing and story-telling and drinking the fire-water – that is the rum – clear into the night. Everybody would eat their belly full, cool off, rest and come again for more. All who couldn't dance would lift up foot seh them a-dance, all who couldn't sing, did a-bellow, even if they sounded like 'when puss deh pon dem season'. Sometimes, if it was a big celebration, wedding party or christening, they might have butchered a hog or two at the same time as the goat and have jerk-pork; that is what would make the gerrey sweet! I love jerk-pork so till. A couple of my friends who did go to Seventh Day Adventist church always used to tell me not to eat it for the Bible says pork is unclean, but I always used to tell them, 'me naa give up pork, especially jerk-pork, for it is too sweet'.

'Trenton', 'Nathan', 'Dat', 'Arnal' – what manner and variety of names they used to have for pig meat. Never was a thing so forsaken and desired at the same time; so forbidden yet so sweet. Pork came in like forbidden fruit; plenty would convince themselves that they never wanted it, only to find a way – or a name to call it – by which they could yield to temptation. A wedding feast was one of the main chances to pass into hog heaven with the amount of jerk-pork that would be provided. Those old time feast days were wonderful affairs, and the one thing that stands out is how nice food used to be. Not any more; food nowadays is bare artificial fertiliser and force-riping, so the produce no have no taste. Even sweet potato – which we call 'pitata' – no sweet and nice today like how they did stay in the olden days when we were working the land. There was the Lewis Daley potato, that one was white and big, then the Cerise, which was red and very sweet, the Cusco potato was a small type which, when it was growing, the slip would run and it would send up a shoot. You know, as you were farming the land, you got to know everything about the vegetation that you were cultivating. The people who used to come a-market would rely on you to make sure a no 'fenky-fenky goods' they were buying to carry home. We all know what we are used to, so that is why nowadays it would bring 'water to yu y'eye' to know how people will accept any and anything, no quality or standard. Especially when it comes to food-kind plenty people no longer bother to try to make sure they are really growing things to the best of their ability and reaping the choicest goods to carry to sell to the customers. From you reach a stage where you just accept anything that comes up out of the ground, you know that in a matter of time people won't remember how good things used to be and come to distinguish the quality again. Po! In my days, those kind of devil-may-care farmers would never sell a thing; nobody would buy from them for people only wanted the best. Sweet cassava was something else we use to grow, and it always had many uses. You would scrape and grater, then juice it and put it out to air dry. After that you would sieve it and it would be ready to bake. You can't use the same knife you use to cut sweet cassava to cut the bitter cassava, not at all. All these things we did know for a fact, but me no know who business with all this again.

A certain man, named Missa Charles Colley, from out on the way to Belmont market, used to give me a whole heap of cassava, and I always had things to trade it with, especially fish from the fishermen at Whitehouse. When I finished, my task would be to go home and make bammies with the cassava, and roast fish to eat it with. For how everybody loved roast fish and bammy, not even a little piece would get kibba up to eat for breakfast in the morning or to be put into a shet-pan to carry to work.

Ice-cream bucket

You can be certain it wasn't pickney alone who got excited when Maas Scottie used to take out his ice-cream bucket. He had lived in Kingston, but came down to live over our side when his madda, Mirrel, took sick. Maas Scottie was such a jovial fellow, never one to give a cross word or to be in a quarrel; and he had a great love for children, especially those who were orphans or badly treated. To make ice-cream, he used to bwoil up some corn starch with milk and sweeten it; then when it was cool, he would throw it in a vessel which was inside the ice-cream bucket and turn that handle, with many a child lending a hand, until the mixture was quite stiff. After that, he would take off the cover and put in whatever colour or flavouring took his fancy; vanilla, pineapple, mango, guava or passion-fruit, and then he would transfer the mix to a bigger bucket, and stack 'the packer' – that is another container of ice – all around the inner vessel so the cream wouldn't melt. My-o-my, how we loved that treat; by the time Maas Scottie was to get out the cones to scoop the cream into, everybody would be smitten with excitement and anticipation. I remember my first taste of ice-cream; oh, what a joyful thing it was to roll that cool ball of sweet candy all around my tongue and then just let it slide down my throat and quench my thirst; licking, licking all the while so it wouldn't drip and stain my apron front. It wasn't often that we had the experience, for most times it wasn't easy to get ice, but when it was festival time, picnic or simply when genial Maas Scottie had a mind to make our hearts dance, he would take out his ice-cream bucket and even who was ole and decrepit would feel sprightly; a child again.

Cocoa-tea and coffee

We always had our own coffee-walk and a cocoa-walk where we grew coffee and cocoa. Cocoa or 'cacao' you would pick when it was red ripe, just like coffee; when you see the coffee berry so red, it is very sweet and pickney would pick the berries and suck them, birds too and even rats would eat those berries. When cocoa was ready to harvest, usually you would see some women with baskets a-top their heads picking the cocoa pods and throwing them up into the basket. After the picking, you would cut the cocoa and put them on the *barbecue* to sun for a couple days. While the beans were taking sun now, they would turn sour. After the drying period, you would put them into a pot and put it a-fire to parch. In the kitchen you would ketch up the fire real good, and keep turning it with a wooden spoon to make sure it didn't burn. Afterwards, you would take it off the fire and strip off the shell, then put the cocoa beans in the mortar and beat it with the pestle to make chocolate.

A no yesterday me did have fi-me mortar an' pestle, you know, I inherited one from ole Aunt Ione, and it is still there right now working as good as ever. I know that pounding food in the mortar is part of our tradition going right back to Africa days; people beating food-kind inna mortar and singing dem songs, just like my grandmadda and her grandmadda before her. Still, I was too busy to bother about singing; for I always worked quicker without any accompaniment. With the cocoa, you would be beating and handling the poundings at the same time, rolling it between your fingers, but not once would you mash your fingers; yu deh inna world too long fi dat! You beat the cocoa to the quality yu want it, coarse or fine, and as you are beating, you would see some oil coming up. If you wanted your chocolate extra fine, then you could wait till you roll the beaten cocoa up into balls (or else in the long shape), then put them to set on some banana leaves, and after they were set, you grater the chocolate and beat it over again in the mortar; by this, the quality would get to be very fine and you would just roll it and set it again. First thing a' morning, yu would have cocoa-tea; well sweet, with some nutmeg and creamy goat's milk or else condensed milk; eat that with bread, bammy, roast breadfruit, yam or even sweet-potato, and you'd be ready for anything.

To do the coffee, you would take it up after sunning and parch it same like the cocoa. When it was roasted to the richness you wanted – me always like mine dark brown when it is really rich – you would beat it and then fan it to get off all the shell. After that, just beat it into a fine powder and that coffee was ready to brew. I always liked my coffee black and strong and well sweet, much like my old man, I always used to joke. One thing, we know good food in Jamaica. And, you know, we might have been poor but we never starved and we always prepared decent food even if we only had a little salt-ting or meat-kind or fish-kind to go with it. Corn, we would have readily enough, and we could take that and grater it to make turn-cornmeal, or else make corn-dumplings, big and flat or the tiny spinners to go in peas soup. In the morning or down in the day-time, we might fry some johnny-cakes to eat with a nice piece of roast salt-fish, or else use the fish to make *stamp-and-go*, which would keep you going till dinner was ready. If ackee was in season you would cook that up with saltfish and eat it with banana or plaintain, sof' yam, and 'puss prayers' – avocado. Ole time people used to call salt-fish baccalow; it was always very tough and you had to soak it a long time to get out the salt before you could cook it. Shortages or hard times pushed up the price, but whenever it was crab season, May month, when the rainfall would drive them from their holes and into your net or basket in time to make the pot for breakfast time, it made a delightful change. I said already that ram goat liver was me lover, but crab was the lover-lover! I could eat two big ones at one sitting, and anyhow you used the crab to make soup, bwoy, that night you would know you had eaten in style. Make no mistake, few places can equal Jamaica when it comes to sea-food. We used to *skoveech* fish, pepper it up and drown it in vinegar, onion, skellion and seasoning. Man, that would get eaten with bread, bammy or roast breadfruit at any time of day, and, believe me, it would go down quite well.

15
Bad Blood

Trouble and strife

Life as we knew it up a' Rocky Mountain was really a working life. Paapa and me were not the kind of people who could just sit down plait sand and stone breeze because lazy people will never prosper, although before they get up and try to make something of their lives, they would rather begrudge you who were trying and draw up schemes to undermine your efforts. There were plenty-plenty such kufenge around in our days, and I know for certain that such people are still about. We went through some hard and painful times with people who never wanted us to even possess what was our own rightful property. Imagine that. Heaven knows, a no rich we did rich, nor had we stolen anything, but from you meet with bad-minded people, anything at all that you have is too good for you. We worked the land, treated it respectfully, and it rewarded us with a heap of produce; that place was blooming with gungoo peas, patran beans, sugar beans, yam, dasheen, corn, fruit trees and a wide variety of cultivation, while another part was under mahoe; everywhere you looked, pure mahoe trees, which we would cut and sell the wood for lumber and strip the limbs to make rope. We used to make our own rope by stripping the trumpet, that is the trunk, put it out to sun then take it and twist it into a heavy-duty rope that was so strong and long-lasting, and had any number of uses: for tying up the beasts, cows, donkeys, goats, or it could even make mats for the house. Paapa organised the lumber work and did most of the stripping while occasionally, I did the twisting. Whenever people asked about rope, I always said, 'me a de twister'. But even that simple activity led to contention.

Now, the portion of land that was planted up with lumber-wood was Paapa's family legacy; it had got passed down and shared out between all the siblings, but just as it was with my family, none of the children wanted to work the land except Paapa, so he took care of the

whole property. Lucy, his sister, had married and gone abroad, setting
up home in Canada. Another bredda, Jethro, was a teacher, the other
one, Joel, had died and *tarrah* one, Winkie, travelled to Cuba, Panama
and Puerto Rico to work. He never had any children because, while
he was off on farm labour one time, he contracted the mumps along
with the whole gang of labourers, and doctors told him that his seed
was bad and he wouldn't be able to have children. Winkie would
always come and go, for he had the travelling bug, but it seemed the
only place he decided he wasn't going to do any work was back at
home, especially if his bredda, Paapa, asked him to lend a hand.

One time a man in the area named Egbert Sommerwell, took a
shine to our place and approached us to sell some of the land to him.
We told him 'no', for we weren't planning to sell up for any reason.
He wasn't satisfied with that answer, so he went clear over to
Plaistow to beg Paapa's bredda, Winkie, to sell him a piece of the
land, whether acre or the whole of it, I don't know. A covet him did
covet us, through the place was so heavy under the lumber wood.
And, let me tell you, that lumber grew up so fast and hardy, and with
the fellow was so business-minded it was easy to see where he was
coming from in wanting to take the place over, so much so that he
decided to go clear behind our backs to obtain it. That man lined up
Paapa's own bredda against him to make it look like Paapa's family
alone was eating off the wealth of the land, a portion of which did
belong to Winkie after all. So, with that divisive story, Sommerwell
went and won over Winkie and together they decided to go get
further support from one of Paapa and Winkie's aunts, Agatha, one
in particular who never like us at-all, at-all, so she was more than
glad to give her support to Sommerwell's emerging conspiracy and
without much ado, they came to demand the sale of the mahoe land.
What could we do but comply? But that Sommerwell was so craven
for gain that he couldn't get his hands on the property for two
minutes before he razed the place; he wouldn't even wait for the
wood to fully mature, he cleaned out the place in quick time. We only
stepped back to one side and watched what did a gwaan. Before long,
a mighty quarrel broke out between the three unlikely *pasieros*.
Winkie and the aunt who had forced the land sale went to confront
Sommerwell wanting more money than the price he had paid them,
but he turned round and told them to clear off, which left them not a

little aggrieved and out of sorts. The next thing you knew, the marvellous mahoe, that used to fill up the whole place, died right out. Over time, the splendour of the place just vanished; it came in like when a virile man goes bald. Soon the land just became overrun with bare bush and it appeared that man, Sommerwell, stood a better chance of begging that wood to grow than he did have of trying to sell the place for a reasonable price. In the end he must have given it away, but to the grave that treacherous Winkie never stopped lamenting how Sommerwell did hoodwink and rob him blind.

Hear him, 'I be damn! dat fella come in like highway robber, to *riall*.'

Tom Cruff

We had a neighbour bordering us called Tom Cruff. He and Paapa used to get along quite well, too well, perhaps, till I don't know what happened to make Tom turn, but the turn him turn come in like him did waan' bury the least of us. His own bredda, Cuthbert, remained best friends with Paapa, no matter what Tom Cruff did or said, and was always telling Tom Cruff that he was provoking malice with an innocent man. Before the fall-out, Paapa and Tom Cruff used to be so close that Tom Cruff's wife, Marion, was our son Linval's godmother. All the same, from the fall-out a row blew up over land border when Tom Cruff decided that land we claimed as ours rightly belonged to him. At the start, we decided to fight it come, and fight it go, challenging, I mean, what he was intent on doing, but he was vindictive. In collusion with Miss Contention and Pilate, our arch enemies, he set up his animals to invade our place and organised work days and harvests when his people would come and reap all that we had planted. Finally, when he didn't see any out and out retaliation, he became bolder and moved the land border to suit himself, setting up a wall as the partition. When he did that, he decided that none of us could take a short-cut across 'his' land.

Overnight we found that the very place we used to walk with great familiarity, since it was ours, we now had to go right around. That was no small thing, for which part we lived, everybody used short-cuts to go where them a go. That man even broadcast it that he had his machete ready to defend 'him property'. And when he had been drinking, you would hear Tom Cruff tramping past our yard, singing and marching like any soldier, 'bam, bam, bam!' and when the rum urged him on in his courage, he would just walk about like a rover blowing warnings within our earshot about who 'fi dead' and who him 'a go kill'. He and that other hypocrite, Pilate, the DC, were bosom pals, so you could just imagine how that ungodly counsel did go; those people could easily eat, sleep, kill you and belch. And Tom Cruff did have a way of trying to use our pickney against us, especially the third boy, Jacob. That child used to walk and *henkah* all the time around at Tom Cruff's place and that man used to feed him and give him things as gifts, but he knew what he was doing; is line him was lining the chile's belly to get to find out all what was going on inna fi-we yard; in a word, bribery. Anybody with an ounce of sense knows that you can get to find out anything you want to know from a child, especially if he is craven. So Tom Cruff was there trying his utmost to inveigle news about home circle from little Jacob; if the bwoy got pot-water, Tom Cruff should know. How many fingers of banana we cooked and what we ate with it, Tom Cruff should know and it was food and pickney playtings, like marbles, he used to 'pay' Jacob, the spy. One time, Jacob and Linval, his bredda, were over on Tom Cruff's land, and Jacob broke a stalk of sugar-cane and threw away the cane band and the trash in some bush. Linval lick after him saying he should have given it to the donkey and just for that, Jacob ran to tell Tom Cruff and that man came and bawled out Linval telling him not to walk on his land in the future. It was alright for Jacob to go there, but not his bredda.

Hear Tom Cruff to Linval, 'Come off dis place, yu faada must find road fi yu walk'. Like I said, taking short-cuts was how we travelled around those parts. The only other way was clear round by Jawbone, some distance off, but Tom Cruff never cared. And he always used to encourage Jacob to be unruly, you know, for sometimes it was *fortyleventeen* time a' night he would come in the yard despite what me and his father told him; under Tom Cruff's tutelage our bwoy was becoming wayward and indisciplined.

One day, Jacob was at the yard with me and the two of us were under a pleasant argument; 'a chew the meat an' swallow the juice'.

He must have been feeling good now, hear him: 'If me tell yu someting yu wi' tell poppa?'

I said, 'What is the someting?'

He told me, 'Uncle Tom seh if yu or poppa lick me, me fi run 'way go to him.'

I said, 'What is dis?'

Imagine that man could bribe a young pickney and plant such destructive seeds in a tender mind.

When Jacob told me what Tom Cruff had told him, I finished all that I was doing, then I told Jacob to go and tell Tom Cruff that I wanted to see him. So that little fellow set off to go look for Tom Cruff dung a gully and before long, he came back up and said the other party wouldn't be long. When he reached, Tom Cruff saw Jacob's baby sister, Rosita, lying down asleep. She must have been only a few months old, and it was her uncle that travelled go a Cuba and Panama, who decided to name her Rosita Pasquita.

Hear Tom Cruff, 'Fancy, yu ha' baby an' ef me never come up yah me wouldn't know.'

Then why would I be broadcasting it, especially to people who made it plain that they were our enemy? Cho! I never paid him any mind.

Hear Jacob, 'Howdy-do, Uncle Tom-Tom'.

I never bothered to make small talk; I stood right in front of Tom Cruff and asked Jacob if he remembered what he told me about what he was to do if me or his father punished him.

He said, 'Yes mam'.

I made a point of looking straight into Tom Cruff's eyes to see if he squinted or tried to make any kind of signal to the bwoy. Then I asked Jacob if he felt he could rehearse the whole thing over again. He said, 'yes'.

Then Tom Cruff interjected to talk to Jacob.

Hear him, 'Jake, me son.'

'Yes, Uncle Tom-Tom.'

'How de argument did go?'

'Yu tell me seh if Aunt Emmie or poppa beat me, me fi run 'way come a fi-yu yard come tell yu.'

Hear Tom Cruff, 'Me! Me tell yu so Jake? Mind yu mek mistake, chum.'

'Yes, sah, a so yu tell me,' Jacob told him.

That man must have called down Gabriel, Michael and all the heavenly hosts how he denied it.

Hear him, 'A sorry a did ever open me mout'. Well Jake, yu L-E-T me down!'

I told him, 'No, Tom Cruff, him no let yu down a damn!' The thing hurt me, you see!

I asked him if he wasn't ashamed of how he was trying to corrupt a young bwoy and for the way him did a-henkah for all the land and he just started to carry on nervous-like, especially on account of how I had caught him out. And the look he gave Jacob – was as if that young bwoy was Judas own-self, but I let that child know that he was right to inform me of all that had taken place, and warned him lovingly that he was always to be on guard for devious men and other snakes-in-the-grass.

Devil's disciple

That Tom Cruff was very stubborn and the only person he used to hurt by acting like he was the devil's disciple was his own self. He even set his wife against her own godson, Linval, our child, all through spite. It was Jacob alone he favoured, because that one came in useful to him; with his carry-go-bring-come news reports.

Tom Cruff and his wife had a daughter named Helen. One time her father must have got word that she did a-breed for a bwoy named Gladson. Tom Cruff took his time and sharpened his machete; sitting down out a-veranda preparing the tool and showing it to all who were passing.

When the daughter came by, he called out to her, 'Come here, Helen'.

This time, you know, he had a little three-quarter smile at his mouth corner, and he was not a man given to smiling any-at-all. Naturally she suspected him of something, especially because he wasn't a man who would talk nicely to anybody, much less smile. As she looked, she glimpsed the machete gleaming in the sun-light by the side of his foot, so she quickly ran off.

Hear Tom Cruff after her, 'Yu lucky me never ketch yu for it would be a different Wednesday mawning dis!' He disinherited Helen, and that might even have been the last day she set foot on his place. Tom Cruff did have heart and liver problems and was taking doctor medicine, but whenever his wife brought his food and the medication to give him, he would throw away the medicine and tek up the rum bottle put to his head instead. She begged him not to do it, but he carried right on till one day he just dropped stiff stone dead. And, you know, every argument about border dispute followed that man clear to his grave, for we and the wife got on as good as ever after that.

Raising Cain

George, our first pickney, was his grandmother's eye-ball – that is Ole Jane, my madda.

How she loved that child; he was the very apple of her eye. She favoured him so much that we couldn't discipline him or do anything at all that would grieve the youngster to make her hear about it. The first chance she got, she took him to live at her yard so he could grow with her, by this now, she was getting older and couldn't manage like before, especially with the old man gone. After George, she took the first girl, Mary, when I had to go into hospital to have my appendix cut. She took the two children and kept them as her eyes, her hands, her feet, down at her yard. That was how it always went through the generations; grand-pickney would take the place of pickney and look after their elders. The long and short of it was children would get raised with aunts and uncles, or with dis-yah in-law, dat-deh uncle or tarrah granny or other extended family members; for better or for worse, and to the very extreme of it, some of those children were abandoned to a life of what can only be called slave-labour, or interfered with by those who should have been their guardians; not all, but surely too many.

Ole Jane took to George so much you would almost feel he had been joined to her by his navel-string or that it was she same one who did birth him. It got so bad that anytime she sent him up to our place, she would send instructions that he had to reach back in quick time; he was not to linger. It came in like she never wanted him to form a bond with his own family, and she spoiled him so much that the bwoy grew up to hate his own father. One time, as a lad, he wandered into somebody's cane-piece and started helping himself to sugar-cane. A man saw him and reported it back, so George's father beat him. The youngster ran to tell his 'mumma', Jane. She got vex and was ready to quarrel with us over that. It was disgraceful, after we never raised any of our pickney to go thief out people's property, especially when his own puppa had cane-pieces and a sugar mill to that. What if the man did charge Paapa for the cane which the the bwoy took, or prosecute him, what then? No, the way the old lady was spoiling the lad was only setting to send him to gaol. It is truly frightening to know how people can set your own children against you, and that no matter how careful you are as parents, you can still end up with bad offsprings although you do your best to raise them good.

Hell and bangarang

It is a very hard and painful thing to remember all the hardships and attrition we passed through. Not even so much the hardship, for we were born to struggle; I never expected to just skip through life only making dolly-baby clothes and organising picnic parties. No, two things I am sure of: that me never baan fi dead and also that in this life, there are many rivers to crass.

But the hardest part to recount is how two of our own children turned against the family and even came to kill us. When George and Jacob, the first two bwoys, outed school and were grown, they formed an un-gaadly partnership. Although they hadn't grown together at home – remember, George lived with his granny – the pair became close to inseparable. So, the two of them set off in manhood to seek their fortune; making their own plans, and set off to seek out their destiny in Kingston. Like a bird with the young in her nest, you now realise they had must flee and so we sent them along with warnings to 'mind trouble' and with sound prayers for guidance. But, as the Good Book says, 'when yu think all is peace an' safety, is sudden destruction'.

George took up a trade as a carpenter. As fortune would have it, before he left for town, it was one of my former school mates who George underwent his apprenticeship with. After he finished his training, the young man must have decided that he wasn't going to stay a-country; like one of those old-time buccaneers, he longed for the excitement of El Dorado, for that was what many considered town to be. Country was too limited for him, so he set off for town, conscripting his bredda with him, to try to find work and set themselves up. By this now, I had become a grandmadda, for George and a young lady couldn't finish school good, but they had a little pickney gal, although before the chile was born he was so fixated that it was a bwoy that when a gal arrived, he made out that he was going to hang himself; even prepared the noose and everything. Have you ever heard such madness and mockery? It was a long time before he fully accepted the child, but once he did that, little Lottie became the cream in his coffee, so to speak. Well, a father now and more determined than ever to seek his fortune, George left country-life set for town. Me no know all what and what went on, but by the time he came back he was a different man: gambling, cursing, rum-drinking and greedy for power; a marked buccaneer. Now, you must bear in mind that because he never grew up with us up a-yard, his character was very different to the others. You know, when a chile gets spoiled – we would say, they get rotten – they just grow up expecting that people are always going to run behind them, or that anything they say or do will form the law; nobody should challenge them or cross-question them. From morning George was kind of mannish and arrogant, but for all that, him did coward no mus-mus. I got to understand that while he was in town, George and his bredda took up with certain undesirable fellows and joined a *lodge*. At the time, we never knew anything about it, for remember we were way off in the country backwoods, but all the same, what we used to hear about them from time to time wasn't too pleasing. Word was going round that the two young men were mixed up with *De Laurence* and they were reading all manner of black art books, advising people what to do to achieve ambition, and especially gain money. That was what I got to understand, but from we heard that they joined lodge, we were greatly unnerved, for our church teaching was to walk far from such things, yet because they were always so secretive, we hardly knew what they were about, and to this day, I suppose the half has never yet been told.

Me seh, two years didn't pass but George and Jacob came back from town with pure bitter enmity and hatred for their family. That lodge turned George into the living Beelzebub who stole away and indoctrinated likeable Jacob, with his laughing eyes and ready humour, making him hard-headed and cynical. George got Jacob as his loyal disciple to the extent that if he said 'kill', Jacob would say, 'dead', and both would pronounce, 'amen'. All George would have to do is give the order and Jacob would carry out the instruction. To control a person to that extent, a no dangerous someting dat?

We first met with the bitterness and anguish from George when he and his youngest sister, Betty, got into a quarrel. He saw her coming from school one afternoon and ordered her to do his bidding. Now, she never knew him to that, for remember, he never grew a-yard with the rest o' family, and more-besides, she did kinda facety and wouldn't run after anybody; very stubborn, so she must have told him to go do the thing himself for he wasn't her puppa. George took exception, and simply told her, 'Yes, Miss Elizabeth, see how yu prime. I soon ready fi yu.'

Some time after that incident, he set duppy to make that chile, his own sister, go drown in a sink-hole. It was only the grace of Gaad that stopped the plot. How it happened was, one night everybody had gone to bed and were sleeping soundly. Elizabeth got up in the middle of the night, and started making to open the door go out. Now, I was a light sleeper; if a pin dropped, I would rise.

I saw her trying to open the back door and asked her what she was doing.

She said, 'Me haffi go out.'

So I asked her, 'Fi wha?'

She said, 'Yu no hear wan man a-call me name seh me mus' come out to him?'

This time the others had woken up because of the commotion, but we couldn't hear a sound, although she insisted she could hear smady a-call her name.

I told her sternly, 'If yu tink yu bad, open de door.'

The poor gal was just mad to go outside; she was fighting and wrestling, even pulling off her clothes and struggling to go through the door.

We had to sit down on her to keep her inside and then the amount of prayers, all manner of intervention to try and save her life because the next couple of nights the same thing happened again, until we managed to take full control and drive the duppy away. They used to call me 'Duppy Conqueror' after my granny, Ma Fanny, because me never use to renk with duppies; instead, I always used to order them to go right back to whichever part o' hell they came from. Much later, we got to understand that George had planned to arrange it so his own sister would go out in the middle of the night and drown in a sink-hole, then he would set her duppy on the whole family to tear us apart. When that never worked out, he came again with another hellment.

George, by now, was the devil incarnate, on account of the way he was living; drunk with wickedness and mad with violence. He and

Jacob, the young disciple, decided to come for the deeds to land we owned. He must have run out of plans to try and use obeah to kill us off, since all the duppies he sent come a-yard, I sent them right back. So now, he decided to come up-front and bold. This particular day, the two of them came up to the house. Their father wasn't there, he was working down by the mill, and everybody else was away for one reason or another. Now, my faithful daag, Lily, was by me, and she never used to form the fool with any strangers who come by the house. She saw the two young men and started barking wildly and making ready to bite.

The fellows hollered, 'Hol' daag' and hear Jacob, 'Easy no, we are all one Jamaican'.

Me seh Ma! This time, their eyes were red up from smoking ganja and drinking rum, their hair was matty-matty and their clothes were hitched up on them like *heng 'pon nail*. I couldn't believe those were my own children which I had birthed, even delivering one of them my own self. As they swaggered into the yard, they came in like strangers, *rough and righin*. I was busy hanging out clothes and just carried on what I was doing without saying a word, except to call off the daag. Me did just a observe.

They came up and greeted me, letting me know, 'is look dem come look fi me'. Little did I know at the time what evil league they were conspiring with to put us off our own land. Those two bwoys – men – were in cahoots with our enemies round about the area that we were to call neighbours, like Miss Contention and Pilate, and even Egbert Sommerwell. The young men made small talk, asking after everyone, and after a little while I asked them what they had really come for. At that, George confessed that he had come to talk to me. I told him to 'talk gwaan' and he gave me some cock-and-bull story about how he got to understand that it was because of him that we had obtained the deeds to the land we owned. I asked him, 'how dat go?' and enquired which part he had got that story, but he was careful not to call any names. In the end, he let me know plain that it was the deeds he had come for.

Lawd-a-massy! This time when you looked at their faces you could see where rum and ganja had them under the influence; not a ounce of reason or self-respect. Although they were young men, you could see where rough living had reduced them to looking older than their years and mashed them up. I told them to go report to all who was advising them that all the scheming was in vain and, grieved in my heart to behold my own children come to this, I told the young men that the road they were embarking on would only lead to hell and damnation.

I told them, 'Think again and turn for it is not too late.'

They listened to all what I said, and then left, but they went far; it was up at one or other ole hypocrite neighbour's house over yonder they went and took refuge.

That afternoon, from my yard I could hear the jubilation and smell the cooking; they must even have butchered a hog up there; eating, drinking and smoking ganja, for in the night, hell a-go pay. When Paapa came home from the mill, I told him all that had gone on. He considered the news, calmly, but never said anything. The two of us just mused over the incident and tried to prepare our minds for all that we felt certain was on the way, although if anybody did tell us what was really going to befall, I sure know I would have never believed them.

Murder!

Night fall, and we could hear a whole heap of excitement over hill which part Pilate and his *cramouchin* posse lived. We never paid them any mind, but there was a strange, heavy feeling in the house that evening as we ate our meal and prepared for bed. By and by, everything was shut up, the animals penned in, when suddenly, 'whoop!', a heavy rock-stone landed 'pon the zinc roof. I cried out, 'A wha' dis?' and went to look out of the window. Before I reached, two more stones dropped on top of the roof and more started crashing through the windows and flying inside the house. Paapa told everyone to lie down on the floor, and some of the others scrambled to hide under the table or under the bed, but I just rushed to open the door to see what was happening outside. When I looked, despite the darkness I made out the figure of George and Jacob standing up like excitable dark shadows out by the gate with some big rock-stones – not gravel, rocks – piled up beside them.

As I opened the door, the daag rushed out and started to tear after them and I felt they would kill it, so I called it back inside then bawled after the two bad man asking what they thought they were doing.

'A no yu we come fa, me madda', George called back, 'a Maas Peter we want, for we not leaving widdout de deeds to dis place.'

As he talked, yu could hear the rum; the bad-wud him did a-cuss.

Jezan-king-of-me-mumma! Then now, they must have got the schooling that if they managed to kill their puppa, George, as the eldest would become head of the house, and the deeds, property, everything, would rightly belong to him. My own son was prepared to murder his own faada, commit patricide, for money. As I looked out, I could see all the lights up the hill, the bottle-torches, kitchen bitches and torch-wood lighting up the place with the high chatter and curiosity of people looking out to see all what a gwaan. We could hear the laughter and rally cry for people to 'come look see', but not a soul stepped in to try and help.

I tried to reason with the two young fellows, flesh of my flesh, bone of my bone, who had joined Satan's army, by telling them to 'fi Gaad's sake, stop all the madness', but they only told me to go inside and to do my best to take care of any sucklings in the house because they never wanted 'innocent blood to run'. By that they must have had it in mind that their faada's blood wasn't innocent, neither their sisters and breddas,or mine for that matter. Me nah mek fun when me seh the devil sent those two young men to come kill dem own puppa if he never handed over the deeds.

As I was to find out later, they did have a gun and blood was to be shed that night, if it came to it, but not fi-dem blood. However, as it turned out, it was their own blood that was spilled and that was to change the order of things. But none of that took place before they rained down a heap of boulders on that house, mashing every window with unseen faces advocating the terrorism. It was total destruction while everybody inside just scrunged up in the darkness, huddled together, all under the bed, praying for them to stop.

How this next part happened, Gaad only knows. As they came to rush into the house, Rosita, who did a-breed, expecting her first child, picked up the machete and just lashed out with it to try and frighten them off, but it bore right down on George's hand, cutting him.

Hear him to his pupil-devil, 'Jake, I get cut, but no mind for the lef' han' is as good as ever.'

But the wounding held them off for a time, as they ran into one of the bedrooms and started tearing up my patchwork sheet to bandage the hand and make a sling.

By now, we heard a whole heap of commotion outside, and the voice of Constable Fagin, the policeman. He bawled everybody outside and asked what was going on. Before we could say a word, he saw George bleeding and asked him who cut him.

George pointed to Rosita, and the policeman called for the machete.

Hear him, like some blooming idiot, 'Yes, I see dat it is sharpened for the purpose.' Me let him know that it was grass it was sharpened to cut, 'for we a no murderers'.

Pushing up his chest and trying to restore order, he told everybody how if he didn't get peace and co-operation around the place, 'more blood a go shed and a murder would tek place' – by his own hands. Jezas king of glory! The whole of hell stood up right before we that night. That wicked policeman went to arrest Rosita.

Hear him, 'If yu wasn't wid chile, I would tek yu go a de lock-up.'

It was as though he never noticed how the house was mashed up and all the damage those men had done, for he must have received his bribery pay already – blood money. We found out later that it was a bare-faced conspiracy that caused that mayhem to come about. More-besides, ole time people always seh that when a person seeks riches from the devil, the lawd of the darkness will require that person to sacrifice a human soul; whether a member of their family or a young child; that is why sometimes people die 'pon a sudden or disappear never to be seen again. A covenant like that is hell's own brand, and for it a man can gain the world and lose his soul. Lawd, see my trials! Of course we had to take it to court, but by that time, there was no sign of George and his bredda. Where they went to hide out, I will never know, but it wasn't hard in those days for bad man to commit crimes a-country then go 'disappear' a-town. Me no know if the lodge they belonged to sheltered them, especially after they had failed in their mission. How they managed to escape arrest is quite a mystery, but fi-dem police pals, like officer Fagin and Pilate, took good care of them. After all, isn't there a saying, 'thick as thieves'?

In the cold light of day we were without a roof above our heads, but at least we had our lives. If it wasn't for the grace of Gaad, who knows what could have happened that night? What if they did set fire to the place? No, for the deeds might have burned that way. Or what if a rock-stone did lick one o' we and killed us? Lawd God! Anyhow blood did kill blood that night, how would it be paid for? They would surely have hanged. As it is, they only managed to damage the property, but we couldn't live there again. Everybody roughed it out in a little bourd-house and in the mill, while a new property was built. It wasn't an easy thing to do, you know, for the place we had to stay in was very small and ill-equipped, and all the while we were keeping watch like we were under siege; building with one hand and the other not far from a weapon just like Nehemiah from Bible days. It was some of the same material from the old broken-down house we used to erect the new one. Me tell yu already seh my life was never easy. But, you know, hard as it was, never once did I put me han' a' me head or ban' up me belly and bawl. Not me, for I knew it was the devil who sent those two bad man.

All I could do was utter, 'don't rejoice over me my enemy; when I fall, I will rise.'

And still I rise.

Ebenezer

All what I saw happen from I was a pickney, made me know that in this life you should not allow a thing to surprise or shock you; for all when you think all is peace and safety, it is sudden destruction. No true? And as long as there is evil in this world, evil things will come to pass.

After my heart finished paining me over how George and Jacob gave themselves over to do Satan's work, I sobered up and became as determined as ever. When we finished building the new house, the time came to dedicate it and I made them call it, 'Ebenezer' – stone of remembrance – and told the builders to leave a mound of rubble at the site where the old house stood as a memorial. It is there to this day.

16
Fly away home

The good fool?

Wicked people caused Peter – Paapa – my husband, to die before him time; all that I will relate.

And you know why? Him was too good. Check the record and see, anytime you have good people in this world, evil people make it their point of business to wipe them right out. A no so dem handle Jesus Christ? And Paul Bogle? And Marcus Garvey? And Martin Luther King?

Ole neaga! Before they use dem power and energy to build, they would rather destroy and corrupt. But Almighty Massa Gaad naa sleep, him know all what and what me pass through a'ready and me still a-push on through. I have already told you how bad-mindedness caused us to lose a portion of our property, and how it was set up so blood came to kill blood when two of our own pickney turn against us, and even how a plot was hatched for me and Paapa to live like hag an' daag, but thankfully, none of it ever came to pass. However, one thing did manage to take root; wicked people used obeah to cripple Paapa and made him lose his life.

You know, Paapa was very much a man of his time; he minded his own business, he wasn't *push up*, he worshipped his Gaad and he took care of his family but he was also very strict and some didn't like that. He never worked for a soul, for he always believed in his own independence. He wanted to see all his children come up to amount to something and not to go through life living ''*pon anybody eye-top*'. It was so hurtful to know that grudgeful people could covet him so much, but he always used to say, 'Righteousness must prevail'. As country people, we met with the hardship that was handed down to neaga people from slavery time. By the sweat of we brow we eat bread, but nothin' wasn't wrong with that, for from you are willing to work you can reap the rewards, not just for you but for generations to come. But, me seh mah! It is indeed hard whenever you know you have worked and gutless people were scheming to tear down all your good works. All that Paapa encountered from people like Tom Cruff, who was at one time his own bosom pal. It is no exaggeration to say that if Tom Cruff had asked, Paapa would have taken out his heart and put it into Tom Cruff's chest; so close were they. Still, you don't have to do anything at all to make people hate you. Just because a person calls your name, and will even eat and sleep with you doesn't mean they love you; most times, it is those closest to you who can hurt you hardest; deceive you the most. And, sometimes, it isn't enough for them to hate you, they will even try to obeah you too. That was Paapa's lot. It wasn't one or two times me did deh a-kitchen or even out a-yard and a mind would say to me, 'go look in the wall' or else, 'go look in the fire-hearth'. I well remember such occasions, for I would always find something hidden there, covered up waiting to do great harm.

Snake!

One such time, me and one of the li' grand-pickney did a come up from market. As we reached near the house, my mind tell me to just peek in the wall by the gate. As I looked, me see a big yellow snake and as me see it, me tek time draw back. By now the child did see it as well, and took 'fraid, but me was the bully! I beckoned to the youngster to shush and took time puddung the tray but I never took my eyes off that snake. I simply picked up a big rock-stone and, poi! me lick out it gut-hole, then me sent for the machete and just finished it off; chopped it to pieces and left it for the rats, mongoose or jon-crows, whichever arrived first for a meal of fresh meat.

From my mind did warn me to look in the wall, I had a feeling it wasn't a coincidence the snake did deh-deh. It must have been set there to harm smady inna we yard.

Me talk a'ready seh if smady has an evil plan against you, dem naa necessarily a-go mek you know. They would simply use obeah to set something to harm you so it would look like accident or mishap.

One particular time me was in the garden a-weed up, when, it is like my mind just told me to go look in the fire-hearth. Me tek time go look for me was always obedient. When I went, I saw a snake scrunge up in there. It was so big and black and just evil-looking, no lie, that

I almost keeled over from shock. Anyhow it did strike! Nobody did have to dispute if it was obeah-works that had put it there, but from you're a Gaad-blessed smady, obeah naa go over-rule. Without even stopping to think, I threw some kerosene oil 'pon the brute and set it a-fire; there was no escaping; it burned to ashes. After that I washed out the fire-hearth and went back to tending the garden.

Dutty bundle

Time after time, for a while, that is how it was; strange happenings in and around the house; snakes, bats, bull-frogs appearing like they were set for a purpose; and all the while my mind, my instinct, informing me of what was going on and what to do. So now, this is how the story went with Paapa's untimely demise.

He never talked too much, but people got to know him as a man of his word. Hear what again, if we was in a contention with anybody from the district, you couldn't make Paapa ever hear any one a our pickney talking anything bad about that person, his enemy, for he would discipline them. It is a peculiar thing, admonishing your own child for the sake of your enemies, but all the same, that is just how some people are.

I have already told you about that woman, Miss Contention, who used to allow her animals do great harm to our property, and how I used to prepare food for her husband because she refused to do it. Paapa let me know that I couldn't feed Miss Contention's husband – who she never used to cook for at all – without giving food to her too. Paapa told me, 'Gaad seh yu should feed yu enemies'. My ole man had such a big heart, and while some would see him as simple or naive, he always maintained he would have to answer to Gaad and not a man else.

One day, he set out to go work at the mill as usual. When he was coming back that night, as he turned into the gate, he stepped on something he believed was a bull-frog because it 'squealed'.

When he came into the yard he told me about it. He related how, as he stepped on it the creature cried, 'Eeeekkhh!', so convinced it was bull-frog, he said, 'A good, whe y'a do inna me way?' But, you know, that was no bull-frog. It was something foul which Miss Contention and her combolos had set for Paapa, obeah no less.

The next morning, I was in the kitchen preparing coffee when my mind told me to go look out by the gate. When I went, it was as though that same mind said, 'look deh-so'. As I looked, I saw something beside the wall. It was a strange-looking, dutty bundle like a raggedy stocking tied up with something nasty inside.

I took it up and cried out, 'Heh-heh! This is what Miss Contention set for Paapa', and I laughed till I whooped. Laughed out loud, you know, to make sure they could hear me, and then I threw away the dutty bundle down the gully.

Later on, when Paapa came home from mill, I told him that I had found the thing that he did step on the night before. He asked me what I did with it and I told him. He said I should have burned it, but since my 'mind' never gave me the order to burn it, I didn't do that, but merely flung it away. Straight away we went look to see if we could find it, but there was no sign of the strange object. We didn't know if it was the same ones who had set it who came to redeem it.

Later on, we learned that the bundle was made for the purpose of obeah; in it was some *grave-dirt*, a dead baby's spirit and something from doctor shop; that was what they put in the kacoma.

From that very night when Paapa stepped on it, the poison from the 'set-on' entered his foot and started to give that poor man hell.

The set-on

At first, Paapa would be going along as good as ever when he would suddenly drop dung and we would have to go pick him up. Lawd Jezan! Sometimes when the pain took him and the foot began to vibrate; every glass, every bowl, every piece of crockery in that house, would just shake and rattle. It was like there was a power outside his control operating parts of his body and like a puppet-on-a-string, he would just yield to its demands. The tremors were unpredictable, and would strike at anytime when the *incubus* grabbed a-hold of him. When that happened, the whole place would shake – shake, me seh, like earthquake. And then, when you went to pick him up off the floor which part him did drop, hitch him up on a chair and leave him there a little while, he would simply drop again. Lawd Gaad, bwoy! It surely was a mystery, but everybody came with advice saying we should carry him go to this or that doctor. When we took him, it was no good; the doctors were as bewildered as we. A long time after that,

smady advised us to carry him to see a man named Uncle Enos, a blind
'Feel an' Tell' healer man, way out at Lignum Hill, about thirty miles
away. When we carried Paapa there, we got a surprise for Uncle Enos
asked Paapa for his name and when he told him the old blind man
dressed back and was good to drop out of his seat. He revealed how
every day Pilate, Miss Contention and her people, our neighbours,
would come to him with grievances about Paapa. Uncle Enos said he
got tired to hear that name, Paapa, and of the frequency they were
coming so in the end he gave them something to set for this
troublesome man, Paapa. Uncle Enos was a myal-man. He could
remove obeah, but he could wuk it too, although he was supposed to
be a man of Gaad. As it so happened, the guzu Uncle Enos gave those
people was to set against Paapa same one. By the time we now went to
get a cure, it had gone too bad and was too late; Uncle Enos couldn't
do a thing to reverse the harm. Me seh, when Uncle Enos heard our
story he felt so bad, for it was him same one who gave our enemies the
obeah that was causing Paapa to be in such misery. We left that place
with a heavy heart; sorrowful, for the set-on was now truly set.

    That same neighbour, Miss Contention, used to have Paapa like a
bwoy; anything she wanted to do, even allowing her animals to run
wild in our place, he was not supposed to complain. But, when I
came along after we married, I saw to it that all that changed. That
made her get brutish, and she went and sided with Tom Cruff and
those other hypocrites against us. I tell you, it is not a nice thing to
have to live smack in the middle of contentious people; that was bad
enough, but from his foot started to pain him, Paapa's life was never
the same again. It reminded me of what had happened to my Aunt
Martha when that witch, Inez Woodley, set obeah for her as a pickney
gal, and caused her to lose her foot. Before long, Paapa couldn't even
walk again, he was crippled, and the pain, man. The pain! All that
shaking and convulsion like he was fitting, and tumbling over like a
young baby learning to walk. He couldn't work his land or the mill as
before, and when that pain struck, we just had to get the *liashes waata*
and clap it on to bathe the foot, so he would get little respite. He would
only get some limited reprieve, but no lasting comfort. Oh Gaad,
how dat poor ole man suffered! But, you know, he out-lived plenty of
those same people who worked the evil against him and he always
maintained, 'whoever sows the wind going to reap the whirlwind'.

And for all he endured, he never stopped feeding and being neighbourly to those people, especially that same Miss Contention. As things turned out, a few years later Miss Contention took sick and was on-dying. She sent her daughter, Regina, to come call Paapa. A mussi confess Miss Contention did want to confess before she dead.

The daughter bawled out, 'Mumma seh yu fi come now, now, now! She waan' talk to yu.'

Paapa heard alright but he never paid her any mind. The gal bawled for him to come till she was nearly hoarse, but he never went. I never said a thing, but anyhow he did want to go up there, he would have had to pass me first! But, you know, when Miss Contention died, it was Paapa's own donkey rope they used to lower the coffin into the grave. See how life goes?

Paapa had it for gospel that Gaad's way is to 'do good to those who hurt you and despitefully use you', and also he believed, 'what a man sow, that shall he reap'.

Free at last

Poor Paapa never enjoyed any quality life again, for he was too crippled.

It must have been about seven years after that his condition just deteriorated right down until he had to take to bed, and sometimes we would have to put him in a chair and make him siddung outside to get air. But as for work, all that he couldn't do again. On top of that, the children had taken to their own trades, seeking fresh opportunities – even going a-foreign, or setting up house as newly-marrieds, so just as had happened to my faada, he couldn't depend on them to take over running the place. He wasn't a young man – remember we were now grandparents – but all the sickness, stress and sufferation made him old and 'grey up', long before time.

When he died, you know, that day my mind did tell me not to go out, but I wasn't obedient.

I did have to go plant some peas and corn out in the garden, so I made Paapa's breakfast, coffee and bread with guava jelly, before I went. When he was finished, he called the grandchildren to make them eat out of his hand (little did I know it would be for the last time), then he called for some water to rinse out his mouth. Next, he took his cigar and smoked some, put it out, and put it by the side of the bed. That done, all in silence, mind you, he sat up in the bed and started reading his Bible. I watched all that with a sense of consideration, but I never took it for anything significant. Before I left out, I called one of the grand-pickney, the eldest, Lois, and told her if her grand-faada needed anything at all, or if he was in any discomfort, she was to run and call me. While I was gone, the old man must have realised that him did a go dead and so he asked the child to help him go down from off the big bed on to the little bed. (He never wanted to die on the big bed and she was too afraid to call me or do anything, so she did her best to help him manage). As Paapa went on to the small mattress on the floor, he stretched himself right out and died.

It was when the child's madda, Rosita, reached back from delivering a letter at the post-office, she realised her father was dead. How she bawled! She was that ole man's hand, foot, him eye-bright, everything, and she was the only one of our pickney who did still live a-yard; all the other ones had flown the coop. It was the loud wailing coming from the house that alerted me that something was wrong. And as I got up to run towards the house, my mind told me that Paapa had gone. I felt a numbness that almost held me paralysed and at the same time the swift beating of my heart as it leapt inside my chest like smady banging hard on a door. As I reached the house and went into the room, I saw how he had stretched himself out, crossed his arms across his chest; sensible and self-determined to the very last. I tied up his jaw and covered down his eye-lids. Rosita, who had just reached up from the post-office tek foot and ran back there, this time to go send a telegram. Lawd, what a day that was. Eye-water flowed like a waterfall, people ban' up dem belly an' dem bawl. And with the grieving came the whole heap of preparation for the burial.

Funeral

> Fly away home, to glory
> fly away home; when I die, hallelujah,
> by and by, I'll fly away home

It was Rosita and our good friend Ethline who washed Paapa's dead clothes. After they washed them, they cleared their throats and threw the water outside. Who fi sing *sankey* sing dem sankey. It was sankey first they sang, after that, they prepared to sing Moravian or Methodist hymns. Up to now I can still remember that they always started a wake with, 'The God of Abraham Praise'. You will find it in the Moravian song-book, and it was a song that Paapa had always loved. When you keep the wake, everybody comes; the place is packed right out. Some bring rum, a little money, some board to make the coffin or food, and everybody sings, read the Bible, give testimonies, and eat the whole heap of cook-up till a-mawning when you hear the cock crow.

Those manning the kitchen cooked rice and peas, but Paapa's share, the dead person's portion of food, was not to be cooked with salt. He must get his feeding for the last time, so they cooked and puddung his share to one side. (If people wanted go in deh go nyam it out, a fi-dem business – after that they would have the nerve to tell us that it was Paapa himself who ate it.) That was how the tradition went, you hear. Just like how it was two people who had to wash the dead clothes, it was two people who had to wash the dead body. But a no bathe dem bathe him, they only lightly washed the body. The water was not to be ice cold, it should be just like how he used to have it in life. The two women, Rosita and Ethline, dipped their rags in the water at the same time and started from the head going down – but one can't ketch a' foot before the other; the pair of them must start a' top and go r-i-g-h-t d-o-w-n, from head to foot together.

Me did a-watch all that they were doing, but me never needed to do anything for everything was taken care of. The widow was not to do a thing for it was already organised that way by tradition. So now, the water they used to wash the body, they had to carry down to the burial-site and throw it away into the grave along with the wash-rags. One piece of the rag was flung up into the air and the rest went down with the water into the bottom of the grave, where the other piece would also land. Yu haffi know how to handle the dead, what and what to do.

The dead clothes, that is what Paapa was wearing when he died, after they were washed, they were not to be hung up to dry same time; they were to stay outside and bleach for nine days, then dried and put to one side. If anybody wanted them, they could get them for he never died from any contagious diseases. Suppose he did have any kind of disease, they would have just buried the dead clothes and everything with him. They used cotton wool to stop the nose and corked the anus. Then they tied the two big toes together. Now, because when he was dying, he had set his arms across his chest, they left them the same way. Otherwise, they would have tied up the two big fingers together. When he was alive, Paapa did always say he wanted to be buried in the pants which he got married in, but they put on his confirmation pants instead – maybe he had gained too much weight from all those years ago when we took our vows. Then they put a white jacket and white shirt on him. But, you know, some people were keen to follow tradition, so when they put on the clothes, they cut out all the pockets, for that is where duppies carry stones which they can use to harm people. They say that certain duppies will come and stone people's houses and that it is in the pockets of their clothes that they keep the stones. I never paid any mind to that, for I knew Paapa would have never done that, but, all the same, they were just following culture.

Now, suppose bad-minded people did want to come and take up his spirit to use it for obeah? No man, they couldn't do a thing like that with Paapa, for that man would have never allowed them to ketch him! Anyhow those shadow-catchers were preparing to ketch him up a-yard, that time Paapa would all good to be at Morant Bay! But, you know, seriously, those preparing for the burial did all that they were to do to make sure nobody would come and interfere with the man's spirit.

What again? They nailed the body by the clothes into the coffin, and me no remember if they did put in anything apart from flowers and farewell cards, Bible verses, his cigar and his favourite 'kerchief and such like. I used to hear ole time people say they even put in parched corn and other small portions of food-kind in the box, but me no 'member if we did follow that practice. When George, the rebellious son, heard that his father had died, he came up to the house. It was the first I was seeing him since he and his bredda tormented us and went into hiding.

He greeted me, 'Mawning, Aunt Emmie.'

I said, 'Mawning, sah.'

Then he asked me if he could go look 'pon the body. I told him 'no' and defiantly put my foot across the door-way. Massa Jesus sah! Anyhow he was bad enough to try and step over me foot! Before he died, Paapa did talk plain that those two children, George and Jacob, were not to come look 'pon his body any-at-all, and I made sure to keep to his instruction.

So, that denied, George asked me if 'Nine Night a go keep?'

I told him, 'no damn Nine Night naa go keep yah!' When he saw that I wasn't entertaining him, he took time creep away. He never wanted to hear me disgracing him amongst his friends, so him *gallang*, and must have carried himself up to the Judas Yard or Traitor Gate where they did encourage him to rebel.

So, now the day of the funeral arrived. The place was crowded out with people from all over, and from the early part of the morning, it had started to drizzle; fine, fine drizzle which was on *ni-ni ni-ni* almost for the whole day. But, you know, at the funeral, the one thing they made sure of was that I wasn't to follow the coffin to the grave-side. I had to stay by the window and watch the send-off, for the tradition says the widow is not allowed to go a' grave-side. And it was only who belonged a-yard, in other words who was living at the house, who was permitted to walk through the back door, everybody else had to use the front door only.

They buried Paapa up a-yard, in front of the house, not down in the church-yard, and who never came directly to the funeral would just hook up out by the gate and watch what was going on.

It was our son Linval and Paapa godson, Newton, and four of his church breddas who carried the coffin. But the pall-bearers were not to walk a' back-door to take the body out, they had to walk a' front-door. Why? me no know, me can't go over what ole time people say, a just so it go; and tradition must be observed. And they can't take a short-cut to reach the grave-site, neither, they just had to tek time carry the body to the final resting place. I wasn't allowed to go with them, not at all. Why was that? Eeh? That is what the tradition dictates, but I couldn't argue for it came in like the law. This time the whole heap of Moravian and Anglican church members leading the singing so solemn and mournfully, while Missa Johnson raised the song for all who never had hymn-books:

'It is well with my soul ... with my soul, it is well ...'

Meanwhile, me and a couple other women stood up in the house by the window watching everything unfolding.

Hear one of the women, 'Lawd, look Miss Emmie not even a-cry. If a be'en me, me would-a bawl so till.'

I said, 'Bawling can't bring him back. Him gaan a'ready.'

This time, I had done all my weeping when nobody was looking and although my heart might even have been broken, they didn't have to know.

Nine Night

So long as you have a death, they always kept Nine Night. We provided what to eat and drink; curry goat, fowl soup, hard food, fried chicken, white rice and so on, while everybody helped to contribute to the affair with foodstuffs, liquor and entertainment. Whenever you heard Nine Night a-keep, people would come from 'all hell and yonder'. Lawd, and many were only coming to get their gut-full, to hear stories, carry gossip, and even to come henkah and criticise.

From far away, you would hear the grater, 'rrrbbbbhhh!' – that is what they were using, along with the drum and pan and whistle – to make music while singing backinny funeral songs. Everybody was in the *merengeh*; pan a-knock and everybody a-sing, 'mine a play we a-play, gal an' bwoy', all kinds of songs and story-telling; simple, wholesome enjoyment. It was a marvellous thing, really, to celebrate life and death same time; for it is not a word of a lie that even in the midst of life, death is all around us.

A couple of the women led the send off for the duppy, telling 'Paapa' what a good man he had been in life and how fi-him family loved and honoured him. Before the burial, they had called out the grandchildren and lifted them over the coffin, telling the ole man, 'See yu grand-pickney dem yah, no come back come trouble dem.' At the Nine Night, they again rounded up the youngsters and, addressing Paapa's unseen duppy, they told him again not to offend them for they were his own kin. Then, they took a big rock-stone and heated it in the fire and rolled it right through the house. They would always do so whenever smady dead to cleanse the place right through, and purge it. The mattress, which was put outside, they brought back in. Finally, they bid the dead man 'farewell' and told him to 'tan a' *Lomas Lan*' till judgement', and the time I really felt it was when a lone soprano voice, clear as my ole Aunt Martha's, began to sing,

'Till we meet again, till we meet again, Gaad be with thee till we meet again.'

The visit

Me never see Paapa after he passed, no man. What me a-see him fa? Only thing, me did smell him; smelled the incense, the 'balming potions; what and what they used to rub down the body, like frankincense and such like. It was only the smallest grand-pickney, Solomon, who we nicknamed Raffie, who always used to see the old man's duppy. That little bwoy was truly the apple of his grand-father's eye, he and his little cousin, Lois. Paapa never use to eat or drink anything without saving fi-dem mout'-water; and he always made time for them, one on each knee. So, one morning after the burial, the little bwoy, who wasn't more than three or four, got up and said, 'Me a go mek Poppa coffee.' He went and gathered some dirt and put it into his little cup, threw on some water and set it down saying he was fixing breakfast for his grandfather.

Hear him with his little baby voice, 'Come Poppa, yu hungry? See yu coffee ready.'

This time, he could see the duppy.

He puddung the 'coffee and bread' on the table and said, 'Here, Poppa, see yu coffee yah.'

On this particular occasion, Paapa's bredda, Winkie, was up a-yard with us, and, like we, was observing all what was taking place. Lily, my daag, was especially excited, so that confirmed something peculiar was happening.

Hear Winkie, 'I be damned! It feava the pickney can see the man fi true.'

Everybody now was looking to see what was going on with the young pickney and his 'grandfather', and as we were there observing and couldn't see anything – although I could smell him; the strange sweetness that I knew was the dead man. Suddenly, the bwoy ran into the bedroom and said,

'Poppa gaan under de bed', and he bent dung looking for the old man.

In an instant, it seemed as though the duppy just got up, and whoosh!, rushed through the window, and that was the last time I was to smell him, although the little bwoy always used to see him. One time, he told us that he saw 'wan lady inna broad straw hat a-carry basket and dress-up inna white a-go over to Poppa's grave an' stan' up over it.' When he had done describing the woman, I got to realise that it was the duppy of Sa-Elly, Paapa's madda. I said, 'Sa-Elly, my blessed madda-in-law come look fi her son.' He did always make sure his mumma wasn't wanting of anything in life and she always used to come to visit us, from time to time. Now, since him dead, she never lef' him out.

17
Better must come

We shall overcome some day

That same year was a year for mourning. Truly. For it was only months that separated Paapa's death from President John Kennedy's death. We use to hear about how the black people a' 'merica were fighting for their rights and how Martin Luther King was like Moses to the people, and how President Kennedy was quite sympathetic. They did have a song, 'We shall overcome some day', and down to we in Jamaica took that for a hymn. Sometimes, we would even sing it at our church conventions. When we heard the news that President Kennedy got killed, man, we took it real bad. Later on, it was the same way with Martin Luther King, for he did come in like one of our own, for how he did a-lead the people and especially because him was a preacher too. I well remember it was November and news spread right round the community that 'Kennedy get shot'. In the evening everybody congregated up at the school-house to watch America News-Reel broadcast, and who couldn't see, listen wireless. Some people did a-bawl. Poor we, so far from America but it feava we did feel it because fi-dem loss did come in like fi-we same way. Again, when they assassinated Martin Luther King, there was heart-ache, after all, we were one black people alike. But more to the point most of us felt that President Kennedy and Martin Luther King were good men. Me no need seh again it was the same way me did feel about Paapa; is bullet they used to kill Kennedy that November but is obeah they used to kill Paapa that same August. One song I remember we did sing when President Kennedy died and when Paapa died was, 'Abide with me', and that moved me altogether. 'The darkness deepens, Lawd with me abide, when other helpers fail and comfort flee, in life in death, O, Lawd, abide with me'. Everybody in the world knew about President Kennedy, but not everybody knew about my husband, Paapa. The two of them shared one thing in common, they were both Gaad-blessed people, and as I always say, who Gaad bless, no man curse.

Independence

Gi' me back me shilling wid de lion 'pon it
an' tek back yu dollars an' cents.

I remember Independence back in 1962.

Mostly we did read what and what was going on in the newspaper, but they did hold some meetings down at the church hall to inform the community what to expec'. In spite of all what we did hear and for all Busta's popularity, plenty people did still feel that Jamaica shouldn't come away from England any at all. Some felt that the country did come in like a little pickney that needed its madda's love and support – the 'madda' now being England, for people always called Great Britain the Motherland – or 'madda-land', as we say. Talk of Independence would come in like seh Jamaica had turned big man or big woman, ready to set up house by itself; and 'no need nobody again'. You know, it was kind of hard when you only ever knew about your own little district, much less your parish, to be able to figure out what all the talk about Independence could really mean.

Busta, man! That Busta did have a way to make it sound so good, for after him done tell it, we feel seh, although we were only a little island compared to the rest of the world, as a people we did still *talawa* and nothing could hold back our ambition.

For two weeks solid before Independence, there was celebrations going on around the country, not even fi-we little district did get left out. There was no other talk more than Independence talk. And when the time came, August 6th 1962, it was a day to remember; what amount of excitement and merry-making. When our new-brand flag unfurled, gold, black and green, and England's flag, Union Jack, got put away, our heads swelled till it felt like we were going to bus'!

Man, I tell you, that song, 'Jamaica, land we love', how it stirred us when we heard it for the first. Wha! A we dat. It felt so good to know we had national pride even though some people were warning us that hard times would follow. At the time of Independence declaration, not a soul did care about hard times, we were just glad for the merriment and excitement and sense of dignity which swept over the whole country. But only one thing marred the celebrations, some ignorant people ran into shops and did a holler, 'A fi-we shop now', and they just grabbed up everything claiming it belonged to them 'since we turn independent'. Have you ever heard such ignorance? Such people could never be righted. But for the majority, we were just glad to know that out of many, Jamaicans were all one people at last, that is to who dared believe it. White and brown and black never mattered; all we knew was 'from yu say yu a Jamaican, yu and we a countryman'. Still, the hard reality was that the blacks still suffered the most hardships, and up to today that is no lie. But back when Independence was announced, it was good to know we could hold our heads up high and raise up our hopes to be smady, the same like those other countries in the big wide world.

Election excitement

Whenever election time was coming up, those political men would always try to win people over to fi-dem side by holding meetings and they would draw people by putting some big kerosene pans full of food a-fire – trying to win people over through their belly! Or else they might carry clothes come throw to the crowds. From some people saw food going round, clothes going round and favours passing round to benefit their area or district, it came in like they never wanted to bother working again. Some came to feel that they could live off people. I never liked that kind of attitude at all for it was bare laziness, and, more besides, the scattering of food and clothes was nothing short of bribery. And the way some people could gwaan wild over politics! Some all carry on like they would-a kill their own bredda if he made mistake and voted for the opposition. What is all that for? This time while poor people were carrying on like it was a war they were fighting, the politicians were just living good and sometimes, when you hear from the shout, they were even friends with the people from the other party.

Election time would all come in like war, yes, and the best thing you could do if you valued your life and never wanted anybody burn down yu house or poison your animals, was to keep yu mouth shut. If you decided to vote against the way most people in your area had decided to vote, then you had to keep your intentions quiet.

I well remember a bwoy they did call Kwesi. They beat him so till! Fi wha? Him was PNP and decide to challenge the Labourites, when dem finish beat that young man; bruise him up! But that never stopped him for he still decided to fight, till they forced him to run leave the area.

It is a hard thing to understand how election madness can influence people to gwaan like that. It don't mek sense.

The Jamaica Labour Party did always have the 'V' sign which people held up in the air, that a 'V' fi Victory. We saw Busta with that gesture in the *Gleaner* newspaper. The PNP used the fist inna the air as fi-dem sign, and, at the start they never business with we working people, it was school-teachers, bank workers and high up society people they did a try woo. All that change now.

As to all the fighting, killing, robbing and looting that goes on at election time, all that is bare foolishness. After a no war dem a-fight. Still, they say whosoever lives by the sword, dies by the sword, and whether sword or gun, who the cap fits, let dem wear it.

Return of the prodigal

One morning, I woke up with the dawn and after doing my *devotion*, a mind told me to look out a-gate. Sure enough, there was a figure crouched down on the ground. Me never know a who, but I wasn't alarmed in the least and me heart never leapt. I wrapped up now to stave off the morning chill, and took meself out to the veranda to survey the situation. As I did so, what did I see but the figure of another man tending Paapa's grave; bent right down on hands and knees picking up stone, weeding grass in earnest. Me seh to meself, 'Hmmm!', and walked back through the house out to the kitchen to clean out the fire-hearth and start prepare some coffee for those within home circle who would be going off to their labour. As I started about these chores, Lily set off the alarm, barking at the front, and then she just pacified. I continued what I was doing and after putting the coffee a-fire, came out to feed the chickens. Hear a mannish voice before me, 'Mawning, me madda.' It was George. Not too far behind was another voice with the same greeting, this time, Jacob, the apprentice. George was standing with his eyes red from weeping, holding his shoes in his hands, with his trousers' front wet from the dew-water he was kneeling in. I only surveyed them but for a time I never said a word, just continued to feed the chicks. My flesh and blood had returned to me, but they were only shadows of men and only a memory of corruption; too much pain and sorrow and the spoiled fruit of yielding to evil; alive, after a fashion, yet dead. My two disinherited sons, rolling stones and prodigals, finding dem way back home, ready to sing a sankey and light a candle for their souls' redemption. Yet, as any madda may tell you, there is a place in love which doesn't have a memory of even past wrongs. The mind can always remember and grieve, but the heart alone can say 'forgive'.

'Mama, after all is said an' done, A sorry, we sorry,' George said, bawling into his chest like a distressed infant. And what of Jacob? Prime little Jacob, the story-teller. Seared beyond eye-water? He just looked dumb and awkward, and likewise his bigger bredda, he held his shoes, one in each hand. Now, judgement is not mine, and if I proclaim grace, must I now denounce mercy? My arms had set its mind not to embrace them and my tongue couldn't find any words, save to say,

'It is right to take off yu shoes, for this place is hallowed ground, but go wash unno hands for breakfast soon ready.'

Easter egg

The return of my sons, to my heart though not to my home, happened just before Easter, seven years after I buried Paapa. At that time of year, we would always set out a bowl to ketch dew-water the night before Good Friday. That water would be special and we would put it up to use as medicine. If anybody was sick, then they could drink a little of the holy water or use it to bathe the painful area. Also at that time of year, we would set an egg in a glass of water to see what and what was going to happen the coming year. All you do was break the egg, but you didn't let the red get in with the rest, then put the white in a glass with water and put it by the window towards the sun. As the sun started to rise that morning, you would see the egg white rising in the glass, and when you looked carefully, you might see a plane or ship, that meant smady was going to travel soon.

One time I looked and saw what looked like a jon-crow, but as it turned out, it was an aeroplane. It was boats and ships we knew about as they transported our sons and daughters to a new world a-foreign. Now everyone was travelling in the air.

When I saw the plane in the glass, those around said I was going travel in a plane. Well, I never believed it, but it did come to pass; so seh, so done. Years later, I travelled 'pon plane go a 'merica, Canada, and England to visit my children, grand- and even great-grandchildren dem for that matter. It is a blessed thing and a great privilege for I cannot take for granted the hand that destiny did deal me. Linval, my beloved bwoy, did tek himself away to England 'pon Empire Windrush ship back in '48 and settled down to life in His Majesty's lan' along wid him wife and four pickney.

Meanwhile, Linval sister Rosita did meet a man and set off to set up herself in Canada, while her two other sisters did get sponsorship a 'merica. Little more again, Linval did sen' for Jacob and Rosita open up the way for another one of her kin, the two new yankee dem do the same and so the story run, till all me was able to parade up and down Massa Gaad world like dry land tourist! But, you know, whenever time I would leave from up a-yard to travel, after a while my two feet would start scratching me how I longed to go back home. As they say, 'no-where no better than a-yard'.

I thank Gaad for the privilege that I got to travel and see something of the world. It is a shame my beloved Paapa never got to see it all along with me. Whenever I go a-foreign and, after a time, I tell people I long to go home, they always ask me how me a go manage climb old Rocky Mountain road, for me not young again. Age no matter me, for I know the road and the road knows me. The only place left now for me to see is Africa, which part my great, great-grandfather Old Hay's people did come from. Yes man, I would surely like to see the Africa people dem, and all what dem a do. Gaad willing, it will come to pass. Until then, it is really something to look forward to. And as we say in Jamaica, 'Forward ever, backward never!'

A Jamaican artisan showing a fan he has made [Royal Geographical Society (Sir Harry Johnston)]

Yabba pots (earthenware vessels) for sale. The word *yabba* originates from the Twi word *ayawa*

Portrait of a Haitian man taken in 1908/9 [Royal Geographical Society (Sir Harry Johnston)]

A Cuban country scene at the turn of the nineteenth century. Note the market women with their goods, atop their heads, off to trade

Wash day by the river with clothing laid out to bleach in the sun [Royal Geographical Society (Sir Harry Johnston)]

the cool of the evening ... a humble country homestead [Royal Geographical Society (Mrs W. M. Allport)]

This image of two Jamaican boys picking oranges was taken towards the end of the nineteenth century [Black Stock]

A community of East Indians in Jamaica threshing rice (1890s) [Black Stock]

Workers on a sugar estate. Note the *bushas* (overseers) on horseback. Brutal conditions often led to cane-fields being torched [Royal Geographical Society (Sir Harry Johnston)]

A Jamaican farmer or beekeeper tending his ground at the turn of the nineteenth century. He is growing cassava and dasheen. Note the bee-box for producing honey in the foreground. This type of cultivation was practised by many country people producing crops such as sugar, coffee, cocoa, rum and pimento to achieve self-sufficiency [Royal Geographical Society (Sir Harry Johnston)]

Maroon boys gathering fire-wood in Portland [Royal Geographical Society
(Sir Harry Johnston)]

Maroon father and child at Nanny Town (Moore Town) [Royal Geographical Society (Sir Harry Johnston)]

Market bound with jelly coconuts [Royal Geographical Society (Sir Harry Johnston)]

Homeward bound from market with his bankra baskets, a Jamaican farmer rides through a banana walk in Eastern Jamaica [Royal Geographical Society (Sir Harry Johnston)]

emembering the days of the old school yard, a scene outside a Jamaican country school run by a Christian organisation [Royal Geographical Society (Sir Harry Johnston)]

Posed images of Jamaicans taken during the nineteenth century. Many images of this type were taken by tourists or by missionary societies [Black Stock]

'Cheers, mate!' This contrived image of Jamaican boys would have been used as a picture postcard in its day (late 1900s) [Black Stock]

Bitter harvest ... plantation labour in Jamaica's cane-fields during slavery was often brutal and inhuman. After emancipation, many small landowners cultivated their 'cane piece', producing crops for market and for making rum and sugar. [Black Stock]

Bush Medicine

Aunt Emmie's Remedies

The herbs are for the healing of the nations
Revelations

ackee leaf   tea bush and effective cold bush

arrowroot   for digestion. Also for baby food; makes a good porridge

asafoetida (horsefititia)   medicinal gum, many uses but most often put on
the heads of young babies to stop them catching head colds

ashes   'pitch point wood' (similar to pine) burn the wood, use the ashes for
treating warts etc.

asthma bush   for asthma

avocado leaf   use leaf and root in tonic

bissy (kola nut)   good medicine for blood poisoning. Grater the bissy, dry,
and to use, put some in water and boil. Strain and sweeten. Don't use too
much too often otherwise it will counteract

bitter cassada   use as poultice for treating sores

blood whiss   good in tonic, blood cleanser

bluestone   not a herb, a chemical used for treating sores, lame foot etc.
Pour it on affected area and 'it betters the sore'. Also, can be given to
animals which have worms, like horses, donkeys, cows. Rub a small
amount of bluestone on the animal's tongue to treat the problem of worms

cane leaf   good for making tea

castor oil   good worm medicine, also hair oil

ceresse   good for tea. Use stronger as purgative, good for belly aches, swell
belly

chaney root   thick brown stump. Boil with other ingredients to make tonic

charcoal   good for wind, indigestion. Also use to clean teeth

chicken weed   good for belly aches

chiganit   good root tonic. Combine with other tonic roots

cinnamon leaf/stick   The leaves are good to boil and drink as tea. Used for
treating flatulence (wind)

clove   culinary uses. Also good for colds and for treating tooth-ache. Use
also to freshen the mouth

colic mint   for treating colic

comfrey   good for colds, consumption, stomach-aches

consumption weed (pepper elder)   for treating consumption

corkscrew   grows winding like corkscrew; a washout (laxative)

cow foot leaf   good cold medicine

cow tongue   good for colds

dandelion   parch, beat and brew like coffee; also good for kidney and groin problems

eucalyptus   boil to extract the oil, good for colds, and as an inhalant

fence stake (St. Vincent bush)   cold bush

fevergrass   good for fevers, good tea bush. Just boil or immerse in boiling water, sweeten to taste and drink; or put some under your pillow and it will 'draw the fever'

ganja   boiled or smoked; used as medicine for treating wide number of ills, it also promotes feeling of well-being. Note: growing and using ganja is illegal in Jamaica

green bay leaf   seasoning used in cooking, and for making bay-rum to treat fever

guinea hen   for headaches/fevers (external use: in the bath)

guinea-hen weed   for fevers, fits

gwaku   juice and use for treating bellyaches, and use in sick bath

headache weed   rub on temples and inhale for treating headaches, fits

'hug-me-close'   grows on coffee and other trees, good for tonic mixed with other ingredients

jack-in-the-bush   good for colds

jockey saddle   cold medicine

john charles   'capital cold bush' i.e. very good

king of the forest   broad green leaf; good for blood pressure. When boiled, has a clear, light colour. No taste, just drink like that or sweeten

leaf-of-life (or 'sleep and wake')   good for colds, bronchitis, fevers. Many other medicinal uses

lime leaf   makes delicious tea; boil, sweeten with honey.

majoe bitters   bitters used for purgative, and for treating a number of complaints

mango leaf   use for high blood pressure

man-heart   for heart problems

mint   good tea bush, good for belly-aches and to aid digestion

mirasmi bush   for treating mirasmus in young babies

oil nut (castor oil)   for purging body, treating worms

oil-nut leaf   white leaf; tie on head for treating headache. Put leaf on area of pain inside out ' to draw the pain'

old woman bitter bush   for stomach problems

peppermint (black mint, running mint)   tea bush, good digestive properties

pimento (allspice) herb for cooking, also soak in rum to make an aromatic liquor. The leaves can be used in the bath. The oil is good for toothache

pimento leaf use to season soup

pine needles good for disinfectant (external use), also use in bath

piss-a-bed small grain dandelion used to stop bed-wetting

primeas whiss with round leaves; good for treating colds.

ram-goat-dash-along There are two kinds, one blooms white flowers and is good for treating blood pressure, headaches and fevers. The other blooms yellow flowers and is good for treating colds

rosemary tea bush and a herb with culinary uses. Mix with other cold bushes

rosemary oil use for migraines; rub at temples

salt physic washout (laxative)

sarsapirilla good refreshing drink, also a tonic

sassafras a good blood cleanser

scorny-groun' (so called because it 'scorns' the ground, and only grows on the bark of trees, sometimes taking over the host). Has many medicinal uses

search-me-heart good for heart problems, and good tea bush

semi contract used to treat worms

senna washout (laxative)

single Bible (Aloe Vera) many uses; as shampoo, moisturiser and to soothe the skin, to treat burns, or take internally as a purgative

snake whiss boil in water and strain. Good as baby's gripe water or use as tea bush

sorrell healthful drink, often made around Christmas time

sour sop leaf use to treat worms, also nervous conditions. Good for making tea; sweeten with honey or sugar

spirit weed (fit weed) make tea, boil and sweeten. Treat fits

stiff cock good for 'man problems' such as impotence, low stamina. Combine this root with others to make an effective tonic

strong-back tonic to boost body and give sexual stamina (there are 'woman strong-back' and 'man-back' varieties)

susumber use like a vegetable (such as spinach), delicious cooked with saltfish. Use the berries

tambrind juice blood cleansing tonic. Also makes a refreshing drink

tree mint tea bush

trumpet leaf dry trumpet leaves and boil for making tonic; good for high blood pressure. It grows on a tree similar to cane or bamboo, which has rings. When the leaves are dry, they drop off

tuna tie on to painful area of body to ease pain. Also good for washing hair and for treating inflammation

ver (very vine)   good for cleansing bodily system and for making tea. Used also to strengthen animals (for instance cows) after they've given birth

wild basil   makes a refreshing tea; boil and sweeten with honey

young breadfruit leaf   good for mixing in with tonic roots. Tied on to the body and it will 'draw the pain'

young coconut or 'drop coconut'   cut up and boil with other tonic roots. Also, coconut roots which grow on surface of the soil are good for this purpose

Disclaimer: The information contained in this section is expressed as Native Daughter's opinion based on her own personal experience and recollection. However, the information is not intended to be used for any diagnosis or treatment of any ailment: mental, spiritual or physical.

But Stop –
Some Jamaican Sayings

Folk cultures and traditions are dying out everywhere. The sayings collected here for posterity are a sample of the vigorous mélange of proverbs used by native daughters and sons and originate in Africa, England and Scotland as well as Jamaica.

A good ting daag caan'(can't) talk cause him would be a liar

A liar wos (worse) dan a thief   A liar is worse than a thief

A no want a tongue mek cow caan' talk

A shine eye gal is a trubble to a man

A so mi buy it, a so mi sell   I'm giving it to you the same way I got it

A still tongue keepeth a wise head

As the bullfrog seh, what is joke to yu is death to me

Back no know whe ole shirt do fi it, till ole shirt get tear off

Before food waste mek belly bus' (burst)   Waste not want not

Big Massa give every man him own mout'water fi swallow him own duckanoo   God gives everyone the ability to do something to help himself

Bird caan' fly and him pickney walk   Whatever a person is, their children will turn out the same

Borrowed garments never fit good

Box fi box is no robbery   Fair exchange is no robbery

Box shit out o' hog mout'

Bull never seh him horn dem too heavy

Carry go bring come always cause disturbance

Chicken merry hawk deh near

Cockroach no bizness inna fowl fight

Cow no know the use of him tail till fly tek him batty   Under pressure, you'll find how resourceful you can be

Dance a-yard before yu dance a-broad   Practise something at home before
 • you do it in public

Delay is danger   He who hesitates is lost

Do fi do mek guinea neaga come a Jamaica   Tribal fighting amongst one another made Africans become slaves

Do fi do mek mongoose come a Jamaica

Dog run fi him character, hog run fi him life　　An issue that means nothing to you, could mean everything to me

Duppy know who fi frighten

Every day bucket go a well, one day the bottom mus' drop out　　You never know the value of something till it's gone

Every donkey have him sankey　　Every man to his own mind

Every jon-crow tink him pickney white　　Refers to black people who hate their skin colour

Every mickle mek a muckle　　Every little soon adds up to a lot/every penny counts (Scottish saying)

Every spyle (spoil) mek a style　　Every cloud has a silver lining

Every tub have to sit pon it's own bottom　　You must be self-reliant

Finga never quick fi seh, 'look here', it always a seh, 'look dere'　　People in glass houses shouldn't throw stones

Finger stink no cut it off throw it 'way　　Don't reject a person who offends you

Gaad defend me from me friends; from me enemies me can defend meself

Han' wash han' mek han' come clean　　Helping one another produces good results

Hard aize (ears) bring disgrace!

Hard aize (ears) people nebber prospa　　Stubborn/ignorant people never prosper

Haste mek waste　　More haste less speed

He who fights and runs away lives to fight another day

He who keepeth him mouth keepeth him life

He who laughs last laugh sweetest

Him no even have dry shit inna him arse　　Said of someone who is completely broke/destitute

Him ugly no patuk!　　He is really ugly!

Horse a gallop yu no hear whe him back foot a say　　If you're going too fast you won't think about what's going on behind you

Horse dead, cow fat　　One person's loss is another's gain

'Howdy-do' and 'tenk yu' bruk no square

Hungry belly has no choice

Idle donkey always a carry cane trash go a pound　　Idleness will cause shame and poverty

If a egg, him inna de red　　Someone who likes to interfere or is too familiar

If me no ketch yu a moonshine, me wi' ketch yu a dark night

If shark come from river bottom tell you danger there you must believe

If yu waan' know how much fire-stick a bwoil a man pot, go a him fire-side

If yu waan' lick ole woman pot, tek time scratch him back　　If you want a person's favour, use flattery

Iron sharpen iron
Leopard can't change him spots   A person can't change their behaviour
Lickle lickle waata bring dung stream
Lie wid daag rise wid fleas
Lizard never plant cawn (corn) but him have plenty
Man no know de use of him bottom till him have boil pon it
Man who climb hill no fi throw 'way him stick
Many irons in de fire, some must cool
Mean man go a market two time
Mek sleeping daags lie
Monkey must know where him going to put him tail before him buy pants
Never mek ram-goat trustee fi breadnut tree!
No buy no puss inna bag   Don't accept something sight unseen
No cuss alligator long mout' till yu crass river!   Don't burn your bridges
No everybody wha' skin dem teet' wid yu a yu frien'   Not everyone who
    smiles with you is your friend
No every 'kin teet' a 'kin teet   Not every laugh is an honest laugh
No everyting yu yerry good fi talk   Not everything you hear should be repeated
Old sins cast long shadows   The past will always catch up on you
Ole woman a-mad fi eat callaloo, callaloo mad fi run har belly
Only fool put puss fi watch milk
Opportunity a scarce commodity
Patience man ride jackass
Plait sand and stone breeze   A reference to laziness
Plate claat waan turn table claat   Social climbing
Play wid puppy him lick yu mouth, play wid big daag him bite yu
Pride kill Miss Mary fowl   Pride comes before a fall
Provocation mek dummy man talk   Harassing someone too much will
    bring a reprisal
Red eye people can never satisfy
Rinse yu glass before yu tek a sip a snail slime   Make sure you are prepared
    for the consequences of your proposed action
Rockstone a river bottom no know 'bout sun hot   People in a favourable
    position don't know the suffering of others
Scornful daag wi' nyam shit!
Self-praise is no recommendation
Seven year no 'nough fi wash speckle off-a guinea hen back   It's not easy to
    change a bad character
Sharp spur mek maaga horse gallop fast   Tough situations make people
    resourceful
Short cut draw long blood
Showoff bring disgrace

Sickness gallop come, tek time walk 'way   It's easier to get sick than to get better

Silent ribber (river) run deep!   Still waters run deep

Sorry can't buy soldier lorry

Sorry fi maaga daag him turn round bite yu

Spit in the sky it will fall in yu eye   Whatever you do will fall back on you

Stolen water sweet yet it bitter

Sweet mout' fly follow coffin go a hole

The higher monkey climbs the more he exposed   Social climbers always
     expose themselves

Thief from thief mek Gaad laugh

Thief no love fi see thief wid long bag

Throw me cawn (corn) a door, me no call no fowl

Trouble never set in like a rain

Two bull can't rule inna de same pen   Too many cooks spoil the broth

What bad a mawning can't good a evening

What sweet nanny goat a go run him belly

When ashes cole (cold) daag sleep in deh

When dem tink is peace an' safety, is sudden destruction!

When fowl mek merry hawk tek him chicken

When puss belly full, dem seh rat backside bitter

When six y'eye (eyes) meet story done   Two's company, three's a crowd

When trouble ketch yu, pickney shirt fit yu

Where dogs are not invited, bones are not provided   If you haven't been
     invited somewhere,don't expect any hospitality

Where shit deh, fly follow

Who caan' (can't) hear wi' feel   Whoever is stubborn will suffer

Who don't like it can bite it!   If you don't like it you can lump it

Who feels it knows it

Who Gaad bless no man curse

Whosoever diggeth a pit, shall fall in it

Who the cap fit mek him wear it

Wicked to me once shame on yu, wicked to me twice shame on me

You can't curse cow-skin while sitting on a cow's back

Yu fi know how water walk go a pumpkin belly   You need to know how
     things happen

Yu happy till yu will soon go and tell monkey howdy-do   You're so happy,
     you're becoming foolish

Yu married a'reddy and dew water kill yu husband   You're too precocious

Yu pick yu pick till yu pick shit   If you're too choosey you'll end up with
     rubbish

Yu po' fi meat yu nyam junjo   Destitution

Yu too labba-labba   You talk too much

Jamaican Songs

'We have always had songs a-plenty. I don't recall dem all; sometimes, is only a line, a verse or a chorus but these melodies always make my heart feel glad.'

Many of the songs collected here are familiar round the world. There are work songs and songs to relax with and they date back to the days when native daughters and sons made their own entertainment. While they are truly indigenous to the Caribbean the call and response songs hold echoes of the West African tradition.

Linstead Market

Carry me ackee go a Linstead Market
not a quatty wo'th sell
Carry me ackee go a Linstead Market
not a quatty wo'th sell

CHORUS

Oh, Lawd! what a night, what a fright
not a quatty wo'th sell
Oh, Lawd! what a night, what a fright
what a Sat'iday night!

Everybody come feel up, feel up
not a quatty wo'th sell
Everybody come feel up, feel up
not a quatty wo'th sell

(chorus)

Do me mumma no beat me kill me
not a quatty wo'th sell
Do me mumma no beat me kill me
this yah Sat'iday night

(chorus)

Gal an' bwoy

Dally dung a manuel road
(Gal an' bwoy)
Fi go bruk rock stone
Dally dung a manuel road
(Gal an' bwoy)
Fi go bruk rock stone
Bruck-a dem one by one
(Gal an' bwoy)
Bruck-a-dem two by two
(Gal an' bwoy)
Bruck-a-dem t'ree by t'ree
(Gal an' bwoy)

Pain a back

Dinah beg yu len' me yu hat
for de sun a bu'n me head back
sake a de pain a back me can't linga
sake a de pain a back me can't whine

Wings of a dove

If I had the wings of a dove
If I had the wings of a dove
I would fly, fly, fly, fly awa-a-ay
And be-e-e at rest!

Peel head jon-crow

Dis long time gal me never see yu
Come mek me hol' yu han'
Dis long time gal me never see yu
Come mek me hol' yu han'
Peel head jon-crow
Siddung 'pon tree top

Pick off the blossom
Mek me hole yu hand (gal)
Mek me hole yu hand
Mek me wheel an' tu'n yu
Till we tumble dung!

Jamaica, land we love

Eternal father bless our land
Guide it with thy mighty hand
Keep us safe from evil powers
Be our light in countless hours
To our leaders, Great Defender
Grant thy wisdom from above
Justice, truth, be ours forever
Jamaica, land we love!

Sorry fi maaga daag

No badda sorry fi maaga daag
no badda sorry fi maaga daag
(if yu) sorry fi maaga daag
him tu'n round bite yu!

Day O!

CHORUS

Day O!
Day-ay-ay-ay-O!
Day light come and mi waan go home!

Day! me seh day me seh day me seh day me seh day-O!
work all night an' a drink a rum
Day light come and mi waan go home!
Pack banana till de mawning come!
Day light come and mi waan go home!
Day! me seh day me seh day me seh day me seh day-O!
Day light come and mi waan go home!

Come missa tally man tally me banana
Day light come and mi waan go home!
Come missa tally man tally me banana
Day light come and mi waan go home!
(chorus)

Wid six han', seven han', eight han' – bunch!
Day light come and mi waan go home!
day! me seh day-O
Day light come and mi waan go home!
me seh day me seh day me seh day-O!
Day light come and mi waan go home!
Come missa tally man …

Fly away home

Fly away home
To glory
One bright morning when this life is over
I will fly away home!

Matty run

Matty run, Matty run, Matty tumble dung,
Matty run a mile an' a half fe go tallala

Come back Liza

Every time I'm away from Liza
Waata come a mi eye!
Come back Liza come back girl
Wipe de tear from mi eye!
Come back Liza come back girl
Wipe de tear from mi eye!
I remember when love was new
Waata come a mi eye
There was one but now there's two
Waata come a mi eye

Come back Liza come back girl
Wipe de tear from mi eye!
Come back Liza come back girl
Wipe de tear from mi eye!
When the evening starts to fall
Waata come a mi eye!
I need to hear my Liza call
Waata come a mi eye
Come back Liza come back girl
Wipe de tear from mi eye!
Come back Liza come back girl
Wipe de tear from mi eye!
Standing there in the market place
Waata come a me eye
Soon I'll feel her warm embrace
Waata come a me eye.
Come back Liza come back girl
Wipe de tear from mi eye!
Come back Liza come back girl
Wipe de tear from mi eye!
In the shadow I stand a while
Waata come a mi eye
Soon I'll see my Liza smile
Come back Liza come back girl
Wipe de tear from mi eye!
Come back Liza come back girl
Wipe de tear from mi eye!

Drink white rum

Drink white rum and yu tumble dung
mi no want dutty gal come fingle me!
Drink white rum and yu tumble dung
Me no want dutty gal come fingle me!
Why-O, why-O, why-o, why o
Why-o why-o why-o why-o!
Me no want dutty gal come fingle me!

Mosquito one

Mosquito one, mosquito two, mosquito jump over hot callaloo!

Yellow bird

Yellow bird
up high in banana tree
yellow bird
you seem all alone like me
did your lady friend
leave the nest again
that is very sad, make me feel so bad
you can fly away
in the sky today
you more lucky than me!

The more we are together

The more we are together, together, together
Yes, the more we are together the happier we shall be!

Jamaica farewell

Down the way where the nights are gay
An' de sun shines daily on de mountain tops
I took a trip on a sailing ship and when I reached
    Jamaica I made a stop
But I'm sad to say
I'm on my way
Won't be back for many a day
My heart is down
My head is turning around
I had to leave a little girl in Kingston town!
Down at the market
You can hear ladies cry out
While on their heads they bear
Ackee, rice, saltfish are nice

And the rum is nice any time a year!
But I'm said to say
That I'm on my way
Won't be back for many a day
My heart is down
My head is turning around
I had to leave a little girl in Kingston town.

The nightingale

If a nightingale could-a sing so sweet
Sing so sweeter than they should
Sweeter than any kind of flower to me!

Black girl in the ring*

Black girl in the ring,
tra la-la-la-la.
There's a black girl in the ring
Black girl in the ring
tra la la la la
She look like a sugar and a plum, plum, plum.
Now show me your motion
tra la-la-la-la
Now show me your motion
tra la-la-la-la-la
show me your motion
tra la-la-la-la
she look like a sugar and a plum, plum, plum!

*Back in the olden days dem always used to sing, 'brown girl in the ring' because they always used to prize people with light skin colour, but me prefer to sing, 'black girl in the ring'. After all, the black skin child is just as special.

Donkey want water

Donkey want water
yu fi hol' him Joe
Donkey want water
yu fi hol' him Joe
hol' him Joe hol' him Joe hol' him joe
me seh hol' him Joe hol' him Joe hol' him
Joe hol' him Joe
Don't let him go!

When his wounded hand

When his wounded hand touched mine
when his wounded hand touched mine
Jesus speak to me
through all eternity
when his wounded hand touched mine

By the rivers of Babylon

By the rivers of Babylon
where we sat down
there we wept
when we remembered Zion.
There the wicked carried us away into
captivity, requiring from us a song
But how can we sing the Jehovah's song
In a strange land.
(So let the words of our mouth
and the meditation of our hearts
be acceptable in their sight
Oh, Lord!)

Sammy plant piece a cawn (corn)

CALL: Sammy plant piece a cawn dung a gully
RESPONSE: Uh-huh!
CALL: And it bear till i' kill poor Sammy
RESPONSE: Uh-huh!
CALL: Sammy dead, Sammy dead, Sammy dead-O!
RESPONSE: Uh-huh!
CALL: Sammy dead, Sammy dead, Sammy dead-O!
RESPONSE: Uh-huh!
CALL: A no tief Sammy tief, mek dem kill him
RESPONSE: Uh-huh!
CALL: A no lie Sammy lie mek dem kill him
RESPONSE: Uh-huh!
CALL: But a grudgeful neaga grudgeful mek dem kill him
RESPONSE: Uh-huh!

Hill an' gully ridah (rider)

CALL: Hill an' gully ridah!
RESPONSE: Hill an' gully!
CALL: Hill an' gully ridah!
RESPONSE: Hill an' gully!
CALL: An' yu ben' dung low dung
RESPONSE: Hill an' gully!
CALL: An' a low dung bessy dung
RESPONSE: Hill an' gully!
CALL: Hill an' gully ridah!
RESPONSE: Hill an' gully!
CALL: Hill an' gully ridah!
RESPONSE: Hill an' gully!

Helena

CALL: Helena an' har mumma go a groun'
RESPONSE: Uh-huh!
CALL: Helena start bawl fi har belly
RESPONSE: Uh-huh!

CALL: Go home, Helena, go home, Helena
             go bwoil ceresse fi yu belly!
RESPONSE: Uh-huh!
CALL: De mumma she weed and she plant
RESPONSE: Uh-huh!
CALL: When she done she go look fi Helena
RESPONSE: Uh-huh!
CALL: Go home, mumma, go home mumma,
             mek-haste go look fi Helena!
RESPONSE: Uh-huh!
CALL: When she reach she bawl fi Helena
RESPONSE: Uh-huh!
CALL: Helena me one pickney dead!
RESPONSE: Uh-huh!
CALL: From yu baan come a worl' yu no
             know ceresse, yu go bwoil nightsage
             fi yu belly!
RESPONSE: Uh-huh!

Matilda

Matilda, Matilda, Matilda
She tek me money an' run Venezuela!
Five hundred dollars friends ah lass
De woman even sell me cart an' horse!
Matilda, Matilda, Matilda
She tek me money an' run Venezuela!
Well de money was to buy me house an' lan'
Den she got a serious plan!
Matilda, Matilda, Matilda
She tek me money an' run Venezuela!
Well me promise never to love again
Call me money gaan in vain!
Matilda, Matilda, Matilda
She tek me money an' run Venezuela!

Jackass wi' jump an' bray!

Jackass wi' jump an' bray
let him bray let him bray!
jackass wi' jump an' bray
let him bray let him bray!
Now ah tell yu in a positive way
don't tie me donkey down deh
'cause me donkey will jump and bray
don't tie me donkey down deh!
jackass wi' jump an' bray
let him bray let him bray!
Now me donkey gaan mad
ah say don't tie me donkey down deh!
Cast his eye on a bale a hay
don't tie me donkey down deh!
jackass wi' jump an' bray
let him bray let him bray!
Now me heart is light an' gay
don't tie me donkey down deh!
he-haw! till judgement day!
don't tie me donkey down deh!
jackass wi' jump an' bray
let him bray let him bray!
jackass wi' jump an' bray
let him bray let him bray!

Gi' me back me shilling

Gi' me back me shilling wid de lion pon it
de lion 'pon it
de lion 'pon it
seh gi' me back me shilling wid de lion 'pon it
and tek back yu dollars and cents!

Chi chi bud!

Chi chi bud O!
Chi chi bud O!
Some a dem a holler some a bawl!

Hosanna, I build a house!

A house built on weak foundation
will not stand
oh no!
(Repeat)
The story's told through all creation
Oh yes!
Hosanna!
rain come fall on it
oh yes!
sun come shine on it
oh yes!
breeze will blow it down
oh yes!
this house could never be (uh-huh)
this house could never be (uh-huh)
it would be weak you see (uh-huh)
it would be weak you see (uh-huh)
(Repeat: a house built on a weak foundation)
Hosanna! I won't build this house
oh no!
it would never stand
oh no!
A house built on rock foundation
it will stand
oh yes!
The story's told through all creation
it will stand
oh yes
sun come shine on it
oh yes

rain come fall on it
oh yes
storm won't blow it down
oh no!
this house will always be
oh yes
It will be strong you see
oh yes!
Hosanna I will build this house
oh yes!

Brown skin girl stay home and mind baby

Brown skin girl stay home and mind baby
Brown skin girl stay home and mind baby
I'm going away in a sailing boat
and if I don't come back stay home and mind baby!
Now I'll tell yu the story about Millie
She made a nice blue eyed baby
they say she tek after de madda
but de blue eyed baby don't know she faada!
Brown skin girl stay home and mind baby
Brown skin girl stay home and mind baby
I'm going away in a sailing boat
and if I don't come back stay home and mind baby!

The river come down

The river come down
the river come down
river come down
I can't cross over
why-o why-o why-o
I can't cross over!
why-o why-o why-o
the river come down
the river come down
river come down
and I can't cross de water!

why-o why-o why-o
the river come down
the river come down
river come down
I never get to cross over!

Daniel saw the stone

Daniel saw the stone, rolling down to Babylon
Daniel saw the stone, rolling down to Babylon
Daniel saw the stone, rolling down to Babylon
Daniel saw the stone!
It was a lily-white stone, rolling down to Babylon
It was a lily-white stone, rolling down to Babylon
It was a lily-white stone, rolling down to Babylon
Daniel saw the stone!

One ton a mello!

One ton a mello
for he was one ton a mello
one ton a mello
for he was one ton a mello

One and twenty

One and twenty
two and twenty
three and four and five and six and twenty
twenty seven, twenty eight
twenty nine and thirty

One two three Auntie Loo Loo

One two three Auntie Loo Loo
four five six Auntie Loo Loo
seven eight nine Auntie Loo
ten Auntie Loo count again!

River to the Bank Cobali

River to the Bank Cobali
River to the Bank Cobali
River to the Bank Cobali
None no in deh Cobali
Oh no Cobali, Oh no Cobali
Tek him down the alley!

Penny wheel-o

Penny wheel-o
(penny wheel-o)
A penny wheel-o
(penny wheel-o)
An den mi give yu mi cushu
(penny wheel-o)
An den yu rub off mi money
(penny wheel-o)
Seh penny wheel-o
(penny wheel-o)
Penny wheel-o
(penny wheel-o)

Glossary

a breed   pregnant
a chew the meat an' swallow the juice   engage in good conversation
a don'na charge her fi it   I wouldn't charge her for it
A from Bullfoot   illiterate
altar call   appeal for people to repent
a mussi   it must be/must have been
a mussi did rum fight   it must have been a rum fight
Anancy (Anansi, Ananncy)   black widow spider. Anancy is also the name
   for spider in general and the name of a cunning rascal and hero of a
   number of amusing Caribbean folk tales; he originated in West Africa and
   is particularly to be found in Ashanti folk lore. He is a spider in human
   form who invariably outwits his stronger opponents by his skill and
   ingenuity and gains his selfish ends through cunning. See also Twi ananse.
a no yahso   it is not here
argument   conversation, discussion
arnest   honest
artical   genuine, authentic
asthma cigar   smoked to 'treat' asthma
baan   born
baan fi dead   born to die
babylon   police
baccalow   dried salted fish, usually cod
backative   backing, support
backinny (baakini)   funeral songs or games sung and played during Nine
   Night (possibly meaning 'back in i' (i.e., back in the grave)
backra   white people
bad wud   swearing, forty shilling bad wud – extreme profanity (at one time
   people were fined this sum for public swearing)
badda   bother
balmyard   ritual site for healing
bammy   roasted flat round cake made of cassava
bangle   handcuffs
ban her belly   tie the belly and weep: a sign of mourning
ban up   bound up
ban' up dem belly an' bawl   customary way of showing grief
barbecue   platform for sun-drying produce
barbu   barbed wire

bare so-so toad a croak   all you could hear were toads croaking
batrawn   clothes, articles, etc.
batty   bottom (English: botty)
batty an' bench   close, inseparable (as a bottom on a bench)
bella   pot
Belvue   an asylum
beverage   a drink of sugar water
bickle   victuals (food)
bimbye   by and by, later (also food saved for 'later on')
bissy   a tea made from cola nut, used to treat blood-poisoning
black anansy   see anancy
blinkeys   fireflies
blue drawers   pudding cooked in banana skin
bluestone water   bluestone is a chemical used for treating sores, especially
   in animals
boonoonoos   wonderful, superb
bread-kind   a substitute for bread, e.g. breadfruit
bredda   brother
brial   briers
britches   braces, suspenders
bruk   break
bubby   breasts
buck   struck
buck dem up   run into them
bully-riging   bullying
bun   burn
busha   overseer
Busta   Sir Alexander Bustamante, first Prime Minister of Jamaica
butry   pantry, storage space near kitchen for keeping food
bwoy   boy
cane piece   sugar cane field
can't see   having eye trouble (euphem. can't read)
cawn   corn. Parched cawn is corn roasted and ground to powder, and
   sweetened
ceresse   a herbal medicine
chaklata (chaclata)   breakfast (or a light meal before breakfast)
change into a dog   lycanthropy
chew de meat, swallow de juice   have a good discussion
chigga-foot   chiggas are blood-sucking insects that burrow into the skin
chinee bumps   hair parted and twisted into small 'bumps' also called bantu
   knots
claat   cloth
clide   choke

coa-tea   hot chocolate

coco   nut (i.e. head)

combolo   friend

coolie   East Indian

copper wash   cane liquor from the coppers used in sugar making

corn   salt (as in corn pork: salted, pickled)

corner dark   bleak or sinister

cotta   circular pad for bearing a load, ie. basket, on head

cramouchin   deceitful, sly, underhand

craven   greedy

crocus bag   bag made of coarse material, i.e. hemp

cruff   good-for-nothing

cunny   cunning, clever

cut me ten   cross my legs (i.e. ten toes)

deh   intimacy, sexual

deh-deh   was there (deh: there)

De Laurence   American organisation publishing occult witchcraft books, banned in Jamaica, obtained through correspondence

dem atta claps clock strike   when things come to a head

dem no ramp   they don't play

derek   witchcraft

devil and him wife start fight   rain and sunshine at same time

devotion   prayers

dibby-dibby   second rate

dideh   was there

dis   this

dung de gully   down in the valley (in a food context, down the throat)

dungle   slum

duppy   a harmful, invisible, supernatural presence, believed to be raised from the dead, an evil spirit that sometimes talks. Duppies originated in West Africa and there is much conjecture about the source of the name. It comes possibly from Fante – *adɔpe* – 'a hairy little creature whose knees cannot bend' or from *ndoki* – a sorcerer or bewitcher who takes someone's life through witchcraft. Another fantastic explanation is that the word duppy appears to be a corruption of doorpeep (something peeping through the keyhole).

   Duppies come from the West African concept of the multiple soul: the soul within the body and the shadow outside it. The soul goes to heaven at death but the shadow lingers near the corpse and becomes a duppy unless it is laid to rest. 'Shadow' is sometimes used to mean 'duppy'.

duppy punkin   a small inedible pumpkin, said to be 'duppy food'

dutty   dirty

dutty bundle   dirty bundle, old rubbish; a bad or evil thing

egg red   egg yolk

every mickle mek a muckle   every little counts, adds up to a lot

eye-ball   favourite

eye-top   a dependant, a burden

faada   father

facety   rude

fancyanna   poinciana

fast, tek fast   be bold, impudent

feava   looks like, resembles

fee-fee   whistle

Feel an' Tell   a spiritual healer working by touch

fenky-fenky   rubbish, rotten

fi   my, mine

fi-dem   their

fifth columnists   an organised body sympathising with and working for the enemy within a country at war. The term is thought to have originated in the Trojan Wars but is also a reference to the extra column of supporters claimed by General Mola when he besieged Madrid in the Spanish Civil War (1936–39) in addition to his existing four columns. (OED)

finny-finny   a worker of black magic

fire-roll   bonfire

fish ku teeth, teeth ku fish   fish look at the teeth, teeth look at the fish

fit yu wid a jacket   deceive a man into believing that another man's child is really his

fi unno   your

fi-we   our

fi-wha?   what for?

fortyleventeen   very late, even into early hours

four-an'-twenty-step   twenty four steps, expression signifying courthouse

four-eyes   second sight, the ability to see ghosts

from Methusalah was a bwoy   ages ago

fu-fu   pounded yam, plantain etc.

fur   far

gaad   God

gaan   gone

gallang   hurried along

galley   large cooking pot on three 'feet'

gerrey   partying, merry-making

gigs   spinning wooden toys, whirlygig

gi-me-me-bit   nighthawk, also called the mosquito hawk or piramidig

ginal   crook, a cunning trickster

gravalicious   greedy, selfish

grave-dirt   soil from graveyard (a powerful ingredient in witchcraft). US: goofer dust

grey-back   old, seasoned

grudgefulness   covetousness, jealousy

Guinea neaga, Saltwater neaga   a person born in Africa

guzu   evil spirit, witchcraft

gwaan   go on

hag and daag   hog and dog; sworn enemies

hard ears   stubbornness

heap o' we   all of us

heng dung   hanging down

heng 'pon nail   hanging off, shabby

henkah   hanker, hang around in the hope of getting something

hip an' drap   one leg longer than the other

Holland Bamboo   beauty spot, a vale of dense bamboo

horsefitititia   asafoetida

hot (as in lick hot)   hurt

incubus   evil spirit

jack-fruit   large bulbous-looking fruit

jerk   a special kind of barbecue

johnny cakes   fried dumplings (flour, water, salt, soda mix, rolled into flat ball and fried)

jokify   jocular, humorous, a joker

jon-crows   flesh-eating buzzards

joyful mother of children   woman who takes care of other people's children (Biblical reference)

juck   pricked

kaapi   corporal (police)

kacoma   black magic, spell or object containing evil spirit

kaul   caul (membrane enclosing fœtus)

ke-ke   lizard

kem   kept mum (that is, said nothing)

kibba up   cover up

kick puppa lick   somersault

kin   skin, i.e. teeth bared

kirrout   get out

kling-kling   The sound imitates the cry of a bird variously called the Tingling Grackle or the Barbados Blackbird

knee-cup   knee cap

kufenge   exact meaning uncertain, probably of African origin, 'peasant' or good for nothing (not offensive)

Lawd-a-massy, smady a go dead!   Lord have mercy, somebody's going to die!

liashes waata   a special type of wood ash mixed with hot water

lickle tenkitita   little fish
licky-licky   greedy
li'dung   lie down
li' pulp y'eye   bulging eyes
lodge   freemasons, secret society
logie   crooked, sly
Lomas lan'   world of the spirits
long-eye   covetous (long-eye water, crying, heavy tears)
maaga (mawga)   thin, scrawny
maama man   mother's boy, effeminate or one who is henpecked
maas   master, mister
mad as shad   stark raving mad
madda woman   female spiritual healer
maggitch   maggots
malata busha   mulatto overseer
mampy woman   a big busted buxom woman
mannish water   goat soup with head, scrotum etc.
maroon   French *marron* (wild); Spanish *cimarron* (wild, untamed). Runaway negroes belonging to any of the groups who took refuge and formed communities in the hills. When the English took over from the Spanish in 1655, they found the Maroons to be relentless fighters who, in 1738, concluded a peace treaty with the English.
Mary McCloud   tiny ants often found in pit latrines whose bite causes severe itching
merengeh   lively dance, party spirit
mirasmi   mirasmus (wasting away of the body)
Moravian Church   In 1754 the Moravian Church was invited by two wealthy plantation owners to send missionaries to their estates in Jamaica. Christianity was discouraged by most planters, who did not want their slaves to have a sense of their own worth in the eyes of God or man, and the Moravians were the first Christian denomination to attempt to teach Christianity to slaves. In 1793 the Consolidated Slave Act was passed laying down that slaves were to be instructed in religion and baptism by their owners – the law was not widely observed. Other missionaries followed the Moravians: Presbyterians, Methodists, Baptists and Congregationalists.
more than John read 'bout   more than can be said
mout-a-massy   mouth have mercy
mouth-water   appetiser, a morsel of food or saliva (depending on context)
mus-mus   mouse
myal-man   spiritual healer who could administer or remove obeah
my head would grow   my hair stood on end

naa   not, is not

naa go, neh nah   not going to

nanas   grandmothers, elderly woman

neaga   negro. Sometimes used derogatively by some black people depending on context, i.e., Ole neaga! is an expression of contempt.

news bug   flying beetle thought to bring good or bad news

Nine Night   final night of mourning after a death. It is like a celebration with eating, drinking, dancing, story-telling etc. During Nine Night the ghost of the deceased is forbidden from returning to his house, but is committed to the world of the spirits.

night sage   poison

ni-ni ni-ni   drizzling

no badda   don't bother

no bring it come yah!   don't bring it here

nuff   enough (many)

nyam   eat

obeah   a set of secret beliefs in the use of the supernatural to attain or defend against evil ends. Obeah is African in origin and the term comes from the Twi *ɔ-bayi-fo* – witchcraft man or sorcerer. It is worked by hidden practitioners who use various techniques and items such as dirt, bones or blood to bring about the good or evil wishes of their clients.

operate yu   give you diarrohea, work like a laxative

paki   bowl made from gourd

palenque   stockaded settlement

pan-a-jar   treasure buried in jars, the location of which is found through 'dreams' or by spiritists

pappyshow   show off, ridiculous exhibitionism

Parochial Board   local governing body

pasieros   companions

patuck   owl

pickney   child

pilikan   pelican

pimento   aromatic seed (allspice)

plait sand and stone breeze   lazy

poco (pocomania)   a spiritualist cult in which followers wear white and are possessed by spirits

pot-water   soup formed by boiling food

prophecy fi breadfruit   fortune telling for food or money

provocation mek dummy man talk   provocation will cause the provoked to retaliate, will cause a backlash

puddung   put down

push up   forceful, domineering

pyaa-pyaa   inferior, second rate

quadrille square dance
quatty 1½ d, a penny ha'penny (quarter of a sixpence)
rassling wrestling
red yolk (of an egg)
red-eye covetous, greedy
riall (in this context) royally. Can also mean hybrid, or a coin of low value
righin angry, aggressive, erratic
rough and righin rough and ready, rowdy
run-dung (rundown) coconut custard cooked up with mackerel, garden
  egg (aubergine) etc.
sof' soap soft soap, soppy, a meek character
said speed quickly, at full speed
sake-a grudgefulness covetousness, jealousy
salt-ting savoury: meat, fish, fowl etc.
samfie man crook, fraudster, con-artist, confidence trickster, sometimes
  thought to practise obeah
sankey spiritual song (after Ira David Sankey, singing evangelist and
  composer)
sar (sah) sir
satta settle, keep quiet
scotch bonnet, bonnet pepper very hot pepper
scrunge up coiled up
sea conk conch (sea snail)
sea puss octopus
seh say, said
shame-a-macca/shame-a-lady also called mimosa
shet pan food pan
shub shoved
shupatta sandal made of tyre, wood or leather with leather straps
siddung sit down
sinting something, the thing
skellion spring onion
skoveech escoveitched (pickled)
slacky-tidy slovenly
smady somebody
speakey-spokey posh, affected
stamp-and-go fritters
stoush stuck-up, proud
supplejack whip
sweet up flatter
swips swept, flew
talawa strong, not to be under-rated
tan a-yard stay at home (tend the yard)

tarrah   the other

tek   take (tek a stock, take stock of the situation)

tek fast   be bold enough

ten commandments   bare feet (ten toes exposed)

terrangle   triangle

timbrel   tambourine

trace   argue, tell off

tucko-tucko   thick set, unattractive

tuppy   two pence

turn t'anks   return thanks

turn-cornmeal   a cornmeal dish, 'turned' while cooking till it is stiff

turning dem roll (turn him roll)   turning full circle

Twi ananse (spider, Ananse)   the name of a deity. Anancy always outwitted his rivals usually with tricks and scheming. His name is also used to signify greed and envy. Anancy stories travelled with the slave trade to West Indies and America where they became localised giving rise to Brer Rabbit stories, and the character in turn was appropriated by Hollywood which turned him into Bugs Bunny. (Author's theory)

two foot thread bag   trader's pouch tied around the waist

waan'   want to

wan   one, a

Wappy kill Filope   from time immemorial

warra   same like warrawarrahit

warrawarrahit   in place of expletives

wax off   polish off/eat all of something

whe' fi-me deh?   where's mine?

who fa   whose

with cub   pregnant

wrap up   be close to, familiar with

wrenkers   friends

wuk   work

wus   worse

wutless   worthless

yabba   earthenware vessel; yabba pot is a cooking pot (from Akan language)

Yarvah   type of church

yaws   sores

Sources

Frederic G.Cassidy, *Jamaica Talk*, Macmillan Caribbean, 1961.
Cassidy and Le Page, *Dictionary of Jamaican English*, Cambridge University Press, 1967.